Science Chatterl
Yrs 3/4

Chris Jones

Key Facts
Publications

Published by
Key Facts Publications,
West Ferry Road
Canary Wharf, London E14

ISBN 978-0-9561456-1-1

Author - Chris Jones

Editors - Carrie Lee, Jill Sexton

Photography and Logo - Peter Jones

Graphic Design - Muriel Moukawem

This book is dedicated to dad,
for setting such a good example
and giving so much of his time.

Acknowledgements;

Special thanks go to Carrie Lee, who inspired me to write this book in the first place. Also to Jill Sexton, Peter Jones, Sathi Singh, Olga Venzhina and Mike Scantlin for their parts in helping to make this book actually happen. I would like to extend my gratitude to all my other friends and family, who have offered their encouragement and best wishes during the whole process.

Finally, a big thank you to the head, Mark Macauley, the rest of the staff, the parents and especially to the wonderful children of St Joseph's RC Primary School in Bermondsey, where I spent eleven happy and rewarding years.

Contents

Introduction

Science Chatterboxes are an innovative new resource that will inspire and motivate the science teaching and learning in your class. They are an excellent way to raise standards throughout the whole of KS2 and if used regularly, will impact on the end of Key Stage 2 science SAT's results.

Science Chatterboxes comprehensively cover, in 'bite sized' chunks, all the key aspects of scientific knowledge and understanding required for KS2, with a particular emphasis on the important scientific vocabulary - enabling children to articulate themselves confidently. They serve as a valuable resource of over 1000 questions, all linked to the QCA units of work and levelled from 3-5 to cater for all abilities, including your gifted and talented.

They are based on the timeless children's playground game, commonly known as 'Fortune Tellers' - (there are many regional variations!) – but adapted to make learning fun and exciting. More importantly, they make perfect VAK activities and will engage children from all learning styles; visual, auditory and kinaesthetic.

Chatterboxes also encourage and promote Personalised Learning by allowing the children to adapt, annotate and illustrate - encouraging them to become proactive, self-motivated learners and to make the science knowledge their own.

This is a resource for both teachers and children to adapt and make their own. After all, that's what we do best!!

Teaching and Learning Benefits

Science Chatterboxes are a fun way of learning, enjoyed by all children. They have many benefits, all helping to create a positive learning experience.

Promote Personalised Learning

Children should be encouraged to annotate or illustrate the answers, using the blank spaces in the Chatterbox. This gives the children ownership of the learning, increasing their retention.

Ideal VAK Activity

Visual: The essential scientific vocabulary, definitions and statements are highlighted by means of different font styles and sizes, in order to stand out. It is important that children are encouraged to add colour and illustrations to the sheets - to enhance their visual learning.

Audio: Children love to ask each other questions, listening intently to their friends' responses - this repetition of the questions and responses, helps in reinforcing the important scientific vocabulary and definitions.

Kinaesthetic: The Chatterbox is particularly suited for those kinaesthetic learners who often, 'find it hard to remain on task'. The whole nature of the Chatterboxes involves both physical and mental participation at a variety of levels; from cutting, folding, annotating and holding, to asking questions and checking the answers. Furthermore, no writing is involved and children do not always have to sit round a table!

Differentiation

All the Chatterbox sheets are levelled 3-5, helping to differentiate for all abilities, including your gifted and talented.

Activity Ideas

Science Chatterboxes follow and fully support the KS2 QCA Units of Study (they also complement all other primary science schemes of work). The worksheets are fully differentiated and can be used in pairs, small groups or the whole class.

There are many ways for using this resource, here are just a few suggestions:

- **Within Science Lessons**

  Starter: Just as literacy and numeracy lessons begin with a 10 minute word or mental starter, try doing the same for science using the Chatterboxes.

  Investigations: Try using one of the questions as a starting point for an investigation.

  Brainbreaks: Chatterboxes could be used as an ideal 'brainbreak' activity within a lesson.

  Reinforce Current Learning: Use at an appropriate time during the lesson to reinforce current learning or to introduce new ideas/concepts.

  Plenary: Use during the plenary - teacher holds the Chatterbox and asks the questions.

- **Assessment for Learning**: Blank out the questions or answers before photocopying - children write an appropriate entry. How well the children are able to articulate their responses, provides a useful formative assessment tool. Alternatively, children could show their responses using a whiteboard.

- **Customise Your Own**: Use the blank format to create your own customised chatterbox. Using the blank format, children could make their own - to help consolidate their learning and understanding.

- **SAT's Revision**: Could be used during SAT's revision, an ideal short activity for use during booster revision classes.

- Chatterboxes are a popular **homework** activity!

Instructions for Making

1. Cut out the square Chatterbox.
2. Fold and unfold the Chatterbox, along all four lines of symmetry. The creases will form a 'star' in the centre of the sheet.
3. Place Chatterbox on a flat surface, the blank side facing up. Fold each corner into the centre of the 'star'.
4. Turn the Chatterbox over. Fold each corner into the centre of the 'star'.
5. Fold the Chatterbox in half - so facing outwards, are four square flaps.
6. Insert your thumbs and index fingers under the flaps. As you pinch your fingers together, the Chatterbox will take shape.
7. Now Colour, illustrate and personalise your chatterbox!

Several other sets of instructions can be found on the internet, including pictures, diagrams and movie clips, as well as written text.

Instructions for Using Chatterboxes

There is no single 'set in stone' set of instructions, here is one suggestion.

1. Hold the Chatterbox and ask your partner to, 'select one of the four science words'.
2. Spell the word out aloud, opening/shutting the Chatterbox at the same time.
3. Ask your partner to 'select a number from 1-4 or 5-8' depending which half is open.
4. Repeat the counting process.
5. Ask your partner to 'select a number from 1-4 or 5-8' - this time, read out the corresponding question.
6. The correct response is revealed by lifting the flap.

Unit 3A

Teeth and Eating

Chatterbox 1 Level 3

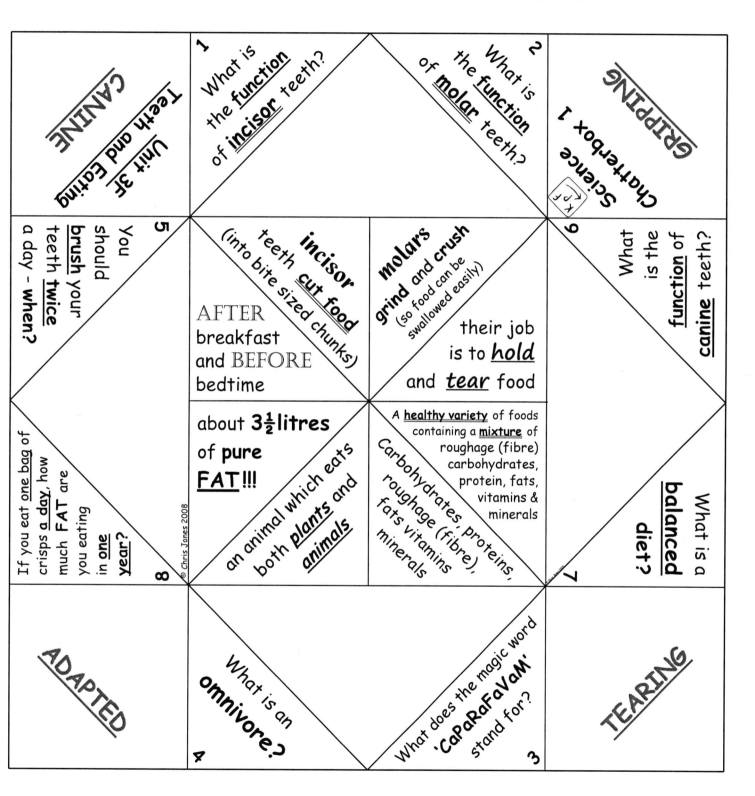

CANINE

Unit 3F
Teeth and Eating

GRIPPING

Science
Chatterbox 1

ADAPTED

TEARING

1 What is the **function** of **incisor** teeth?

2 What is the **function** of **molar** teeth?

3 What does the magic word **'CaPaRaFaVaM'** stand for?

4 What is an **omnivore?**

5 You should **brush** your teeth **twice** a day - **when?**

6 What is the **function** of **canine** teeth?

7 What is a **balanced diet?**

8 If you eat one bag of crisps a day, how much **FAT** are you eating in **one year?**

incisor teeth **cut food** (into bite sized chunks)

molars grind and **crush** (so food can be swallowed easily)

AFTER breakfast and BEFORE bedtime

their job is to ***hold*** and ***tear*** food

about **3½ litres** of **pure FAT!!!**

an animal which eats both ***plants*** and ***animals***

A **healthy variety** of foods containing a **mixture** of roughage (fibre) carbohydrates, protein, fats, vitamins & minerals

Carbohydrates, proteins, roughage (fibre), fats vitamins minerals

Unit 3A

Teeth and Eating

Chatterbox 2 Level 3

PREMOLARS Unit 3F Teeth and Eating	1 What is the function of **carbohydrates?**	2 How are **canine** teeth **adapted** for their purpose?	MOLAR Science Chatterbox 2
5 What do we call **bacteria** that causes **tooth decay?**	**carbohydrates** give our body **energy** plaque	they are **pointed** for **holding** and **tearing** molars are ***flat topped*** for **grinding** and **crushing**	6 How are **molar** teeth **adapted** for their purpose?
What is the **function** of **protein?** 8	**protein** is vital for ***growth*** and ***repair*** an animal that eats **other animals** (meat)	an animal that **only eats** ***plants*** they are **sharp** for **cutting**	What is a **herbivore?** 7
CRUSHING	What is a **carnivore?** 4	How are ***incisor*** teeth ***adapted*** for their purpose? 3	GRINDING

Unit 3A

Teeth and Eating

Chatterbox 3 Level 3

CUTTING

Teeth and Eating

Unit 3F

1 What is the **function** of **roughage** (fibre)?

2 Why should **vegetables** be part of a **healthy diet?**

ENERGY

Science Chatterbox 3

5 What is the **function** of **vitamins?**

roughage **cannot** be **digested** and passes through us, keeping our **intestines** clean and healthy

vitamins are needed in small amounts for **good health**

they are an excellent source of **vitamins, minerals & roughage**

by **flossing**

6 How can you remove the 'difficult to reach' **bacteria between** the teeth?

8 How many **calories** a day does an average child need?

about **2000 calories**

minerals are needed for **teeth strong bones**, and a **healthy nervous system**

fats provide **energy**

they are an **excellent source** of **vitamins** and **minerals**

7 What is the **function** of **fats?**

© Chris Jones 2008

INCISOR

4 What is the **function** of **minerals?**

3 Why are **fruits** a **vital** part of a **healthy diet?**

CARBOHYDRATE

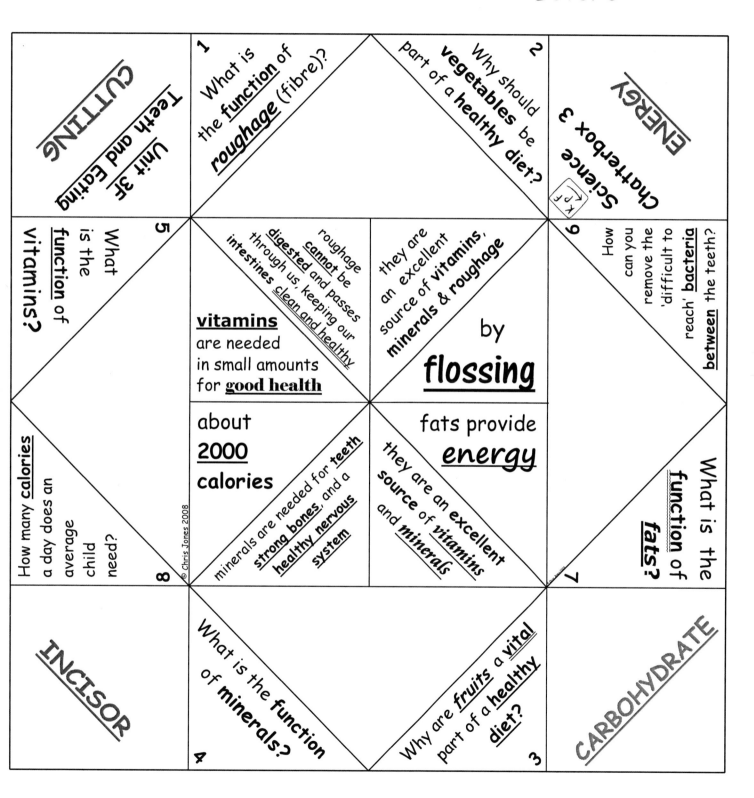

Unit 3A

Teeth and Eating

Chatterbox 4 Level 3

BALANCED

Unit 3F Teeth and Eating

REPAIR

Science Chatterbox 4

PROTEIN

GROWTH

1 How does the **amount of staining** affect the **amount of cleaning** that a tooth needs?

2 Name some food types that provide **carbohydrates**

3 Name some foods that provide **roughage (fibre)**

4 If you eat 1 chocolate bar or similar every day, how much **sugar** & **fat** do you eat in **1 year?**

5 Name **two food groups** which are an excellent source of **vitamins**

6 Name some foods that provide **fats**

7 Name some foods that provide **proteins**

8 Which name is given to your **first** set of teeth?

the **more** a tooth is stained, the **more** brushing it requires

bread, pasta, rice, potatoes, cereals

crisps, butter, burgers, cream, cakes.

ALL *fruit* and *vegetables*

milk teeth

meat, cheese, eggs, fish, beans, nuts.

all ***vegetables*** and most ***fruits***

5 litres of **fat** and **12 Kg** of **sugar** **!!!!!**

Unit 3A

Teeth and Eating

Chatterbox 5 Level 4

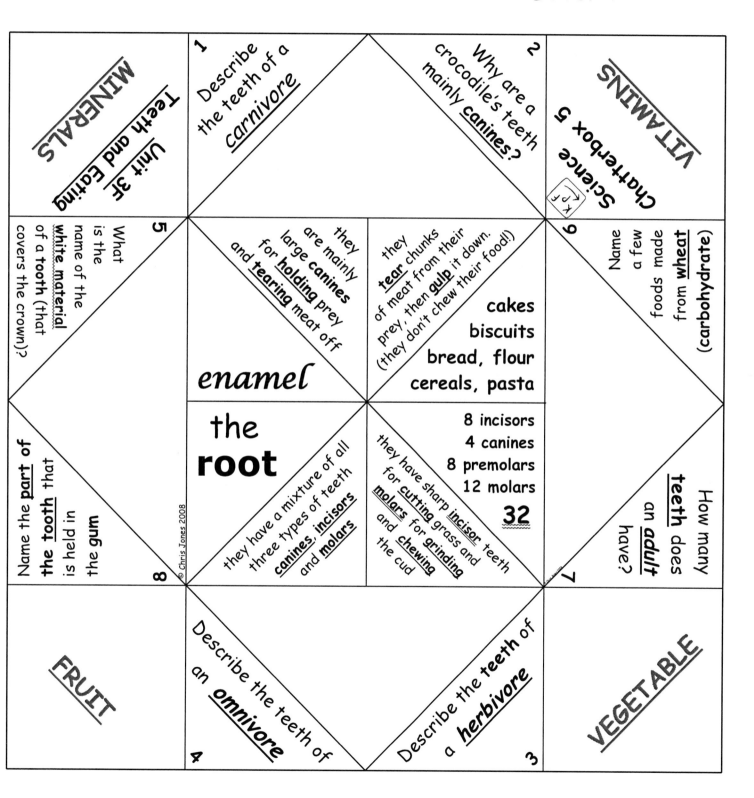

MINERALS

Unit 3F Teeth and Eating

1 Describe the teeth of a **carnivore**

2 Why are a crocodile's teeth mainly **canines**?

VITAMINS

Science Chatterbox 5

5 What is the name of the **white material** of a **tooth** (that covers the crown)?

they are mainly large **canines** for **holding** prey and **tearing** meat off

enamel

they **tear** chunks of meat from their prey, then **gulp** it down. (they don't chew their food!)

cakes
biscuits
bread, flour
cereals, pasta

6 Name a few foods made from **wheat** (carbohydrate)

8 Name the **part** of **the tooth** that is held in the **gum**

the **root**

they have a mixture of all three types of teeth **canines**, **incisors** and **molars**

they have sharp **incisor** teeth for **cutting** grass and **molars** for **grinding** and **chewing** the cud

8 incisors
4 canines
8 premolars
12 molars
32

7 How many **teeth** does an **adult** have?

FRUIT

4 Describe the teeth of an **omnivore**

3 Describe the **teeth** of a **herbivore**

VEGETABLE

Unit 3A

Teeth and Eating

Chatterbox 6 Level 4

CARNIVORE

Unit 3F Teeth and Eating

1 Why does a horse only have **incisors** and **molars?**

2 How does the **'grittiness'** of a toothpaste **affect** how well it **cleans?**

HERBIVORE

Science Chatterbox 6

5 Why is a chocolate bar a **bad choice** for a **snack?**

a horse **cuts** grass, then **chews** and **grinds** it - before it swallows. (canines aren't needed)

because sugar is released **very quickly**, and then you **feel hungry** again - **very quickly**!

the more **gritty** it feels, the **better** it cleans

the **CROWN**

6 Name the **part** of a **tooth** which is **visible above** the **gum**

8 What is the **hardest substance** in the human body?

the **ENAMEL** on teeth

sugar is ***released slowly*** so it **stops** you from **feeling hungry** - it keeps you going!

fluorine

they **rip** and **tear** chunks off - then swallow. (they don't chew their food!)

7 Which **chemical** is **added to water** to **strengthen** our teeth?

DIET

4 Why is a piece of fruit a **good choice** for a snack?

3 Why do sharks only have **canine** teeth?

OMNIVORE

Unit 3B

Helping Plants Grow Well

Chatterbox 1   Level 3

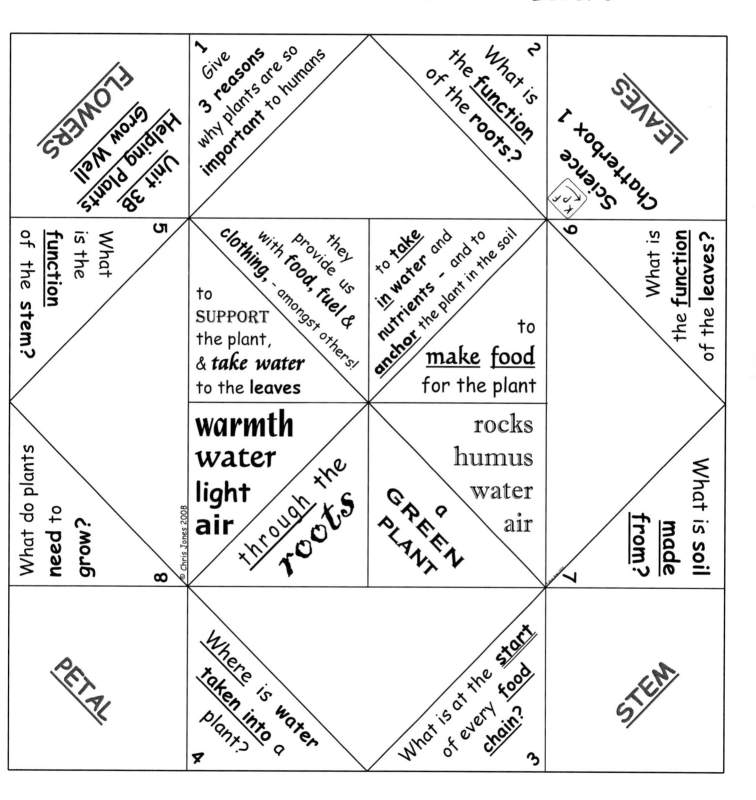

FLOWERS

Helping Plants Grow Well

Unit 3B

1 Give **3 reasons** why plants are so **important** to humans

2 What is the **function** of the **roots?**

LEAVES

Science Chatterbox 1

5 What is the **function** of the **stem?**

they provide us with **food, fuel &** **clothing,** - amongst others!

to SUPPORT the plant, & ***take water*** to the **leaves**

to **take** **in water** and **nutrients** - and to **anchor** the plant in the soil

to **make food** for the plant

6 What is the **function** of the **leaves?**

8 What do plants **need to grow?**

warmth
water
light
air

through the ***roots***

a **GREEN PLANT**

rocks
humus
water
air

7 What is soil **made from?**

© Chris Jones 2008

PETAL

4 **Where** is **water taken into** a plant?

3 What is at the **start** of every **food chain?**

STEM

Unit 3B

Helping Plants Grow Well

Chatterbox 2 Level 3

Unit 3B Helping Plants Grow Well

ROOT

SEEDS

Science Chatterbox 2

SEEDLING

SHOOT

1 Which is the **important part** of a plant for **reproduction?**

2 Name a **seed** that is deliberately **buried** then often **forgotten about**

3 Name a **fruit** with its **seeds** on the **outside**

4 Name some plants whose **roots** we **eat**

5 Why do some **stems** have **thorns?**

6 What does a new plant **grow from?**

7 Which is the **largest seed** in the world?

8 Why are flowers often **brightly coloured?**

the **flower**

they are for **protection**

an acorn (buried by squirrels!)

a **seed**

to **ATTRACT** insects

potatoes, beetroot carrots, onions parsnips

a **coconut**

strawberry

Unit 3B

Helping Plants Grow Well

Chatterbox 3 Level 3

POLLINATION

Unit 3B Helping Plants Grow Well

1 Which **part** of a plant **anchors** it to **the ground?**

2 Which part of a plant **makes its own food?**

REPRODUCTION

Science Chatterbox 3

5 What is a **deciduous tree?**

the ROOTS

a tree which **sheds its leaves in winter**

the leaves

the roots

6 Which part of a plant **takes in water and nutrients?**

8 Which **part** of a plant helps to **support it?**

© Chris Jones 2008

the STEM

a tree which **doesn't lose its leaves in winter** (like fir trees)

petals

the PRODUCER

7 What are the **bright coloured parts** of **flowers** called?

GERMINATION

4 What is an **'evergreen' tree?**

3 What do we call the green plant at the **start** of **a food chain?**

PHOTOSYNTHESIS

Unit 3B

Helping Plants Grow Well

Chatterbox 4 Level 4

Unit 3B
Helping Plants
Grow Well
WARMTH

1 How is plant **growth** **affected** by **temperature?**

2 Name the **key variables** that **affect** the ***healthy*** *growth of plants*

GERMINATION
Science Chatterbox 4

5 What is the **process** called when plants **make their own food?**

the **warmer** the **temperature**, the **FASTER THE GROWTH**

the amount of **water**, **warmth**, **light** and **type of soil**

6 What are the **two main ways** plants are **pollinated?**

PHOTOSYNTHESIS

pollen is **carried** either by **wind** or by insects

a ***lack*** of **water**

germination

they give us: **oxygen**, **food**, **fuel**, **medicines**, **wood**, **clothes**, **paper**, and many others!

the **pollen** from the **male part** of a plant **lands** on the **female part**

8 What could **cause** a **plant to wilt?**

7 What is the name of the process where a **seed starts to grow?**

© Chris Jones 2008

OXYGEN

4 Why are **plants** so **important to us?**

3 What happens during **pollination?**

WATER

Unit 3B

Helping Plants Grow Well

Chatterbox 5 Level 4

INSECTS

Unit 3B Helping Plants Grow Well

1 Where is water **transported** through a plant?

2 In which **life process** is the **flower** very **important** to the plant?

POLLINATION

Science Chatterbox 5

5 What might **cause** the **leaves** of a plant to **turn yellow?**

through the **Stem**

a **lack** of LIGHT

reproduction

it will begin to **wilt**

6 What is the **effect** of **not watering** a plant?

8 What does a seed **need** to **germinate?**

WOW - warmth oxygen water

they are important in *reproduction*, they *grow into new plants*

dandelion (parachute!) **sycamore** (wings)

the **root**

7 When a seed begins to **germinate**, which **part** of the plant is the **first** to **emerge?**

POLLEN

4 What is the **function** of the **seeds?**

3 Name **two seeds** which are **adapted** to be **carried** by the **wind**

WIND

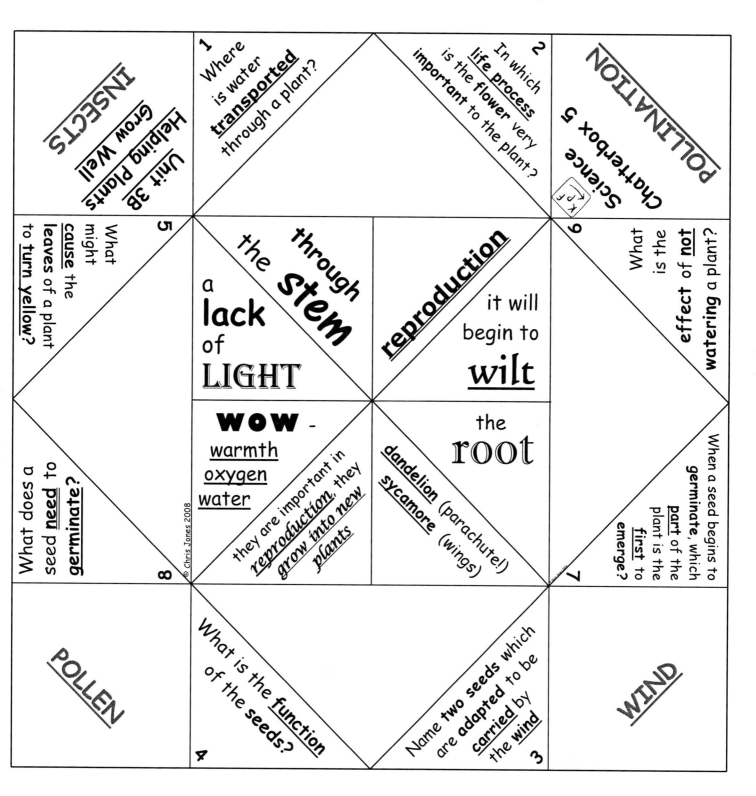

Unit 3B

Helping Plants Grow Well

Chatterbox 6 Level 4

ONIONS

Unit 3B Helping Plants Grow Well

ROOTS

Science Chatterbox 6

POTATO

CARROTS

1 In which **ways** are **seeds adapted to spread?**

2 What is the **oldest living thing** in Britain?

3 The outer 'skin' of a tree trunk is called the **bark** - what is its **main function?**

4 What is the **sweet sticky liquid** that flowers can make to **attract insects?**

5 Name a seed **covered in hooks** - so it **can attach to passing animals**

6 What is meant by **germination?**

7 When a tree is cut down, **how can you tell how old it is?**

8 What **prevents** plants from **growing well in winter?**

by **explosion, wind, water**, being **eaten** then **excreted**, **sticking** to an animal or bird, or being **buried** then forgotten!

a **yew tree** in **Fortingal** in **Scotland** - more than **3,000 years old** (apparently)

it's the process where a ***seed starts to grow***

burdock

it's ***TOO COLD*** - and **not enough hours of daylight**

nectar

count the number of growth rings on the stump if you count 50 - it is 50 yrs old!

to **prevent** the tree from **drying out** and to help **protect it from disease**

Unit 3B

Helping Plants Grow Well

Chatterbox 7 Level 5

CONIFEROUS

Unit 3B Helping Plants Grow Well

1 How could you show that **water passes out of the leaves of a plant?**

2 How does the **amount of space for roots affect** a plant's size?

PHOTOSYNTHESIS

Science Chatterbox 7

5 What is the major **difference** between **fungi** and **plants?**

tie a clear plastic bag around a leaf and **observe** - **water will condensate** onto the bag

fungi cannot make their own food (can't photosynthesise) So some break down dead matter, while others feed on living things!

the **more space** there is for the roots, **the larger a plant can grow**

oxygen (O_2)

6 **Which gas** is **released** by the leaves of a plant, as it **makes its own food?**

8 Why do plants always **produce many seeds** (sometimes millions)?

to **increase** the **chances** of new plants growing and actually **surviving**

the **larger** the number of plants, the **smaller** their size

© Chris Jones 2008

chlorophyll

carbon dioxide (CO_2)

7 What is the name of the **green pigment** in leaves?

CHLOROPHYLL

4 How does the **number** of plants in a **given area affect their size?**

3 *Which gas* is **taken in** by the leaves of a plant as it **makes its own food?**

DECIDUOUS

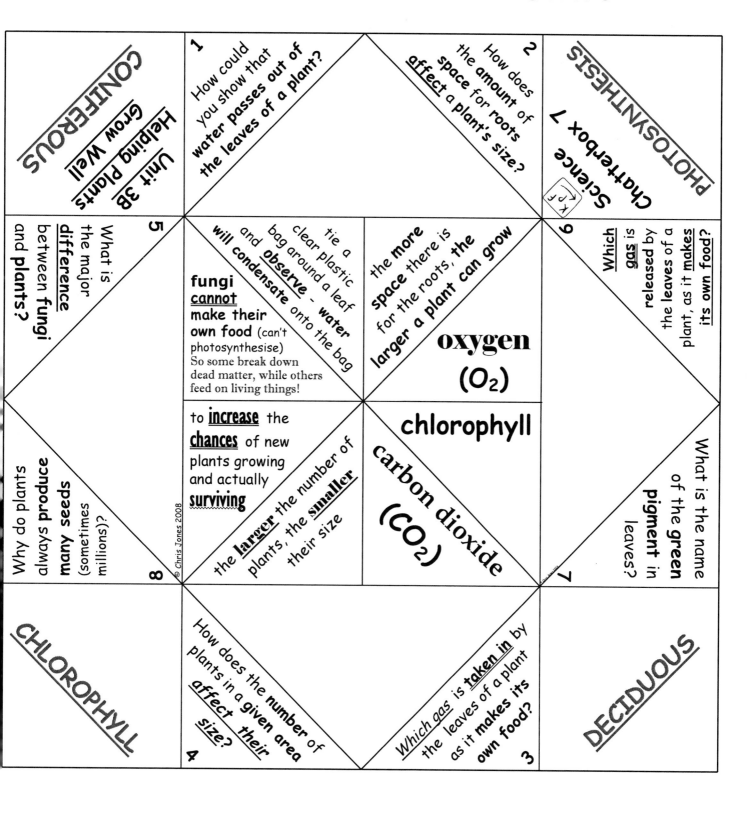

Unit 3C

Characteristics of Materials

Chatterbox 1 Level 3

ELASTIC

Unit 3C Characteristics of Materials

1 Explain what an **elastic** material is

2 What are the **characteristics** of a **strong** material?

RIGID

Science Chatterbox 1

5 The word that describes the **characteristics** of a material is ...?

a material which can be **stretched**, but will **return back** to its shape

PROPERTY

a material which will NOT **break or crack** unless **a strong force is used**

A material which will **not bend** **unless** a **strong force is used**

6 Explain what a **rigid** material is

8 Explain what a **flexible** material is

a material which can **bend** without breaking

a material which **allows some light**, but **not all**, to **pass through**

A material which **doesn't allow any light** to pass through

a material which **allows ALL the light through**

7 Explain what an **opaque** material is

FLEXIBLE

4 Explain what a **translucent** material is

3 Explain what a **transparent** material is

MATERIAL

Unit 3C

Characteristics of Materials

Chatterbox 2 Level 3

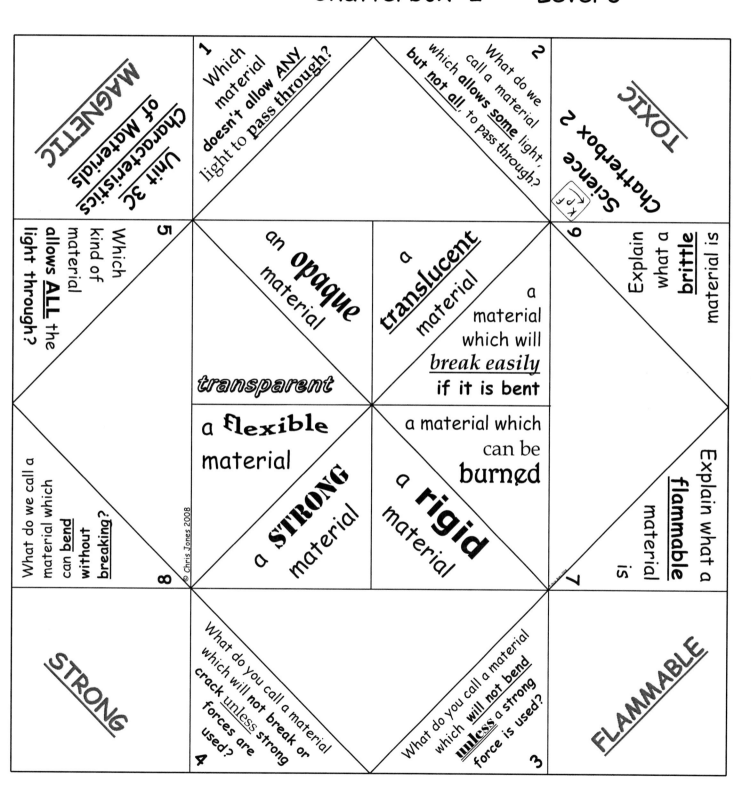

MAGNETIC

Unit 3C Characteristics of Materials

1 Which material **doesn't allow ANY** light to **pass through?**

2 What do we call a material which **allows some** light, **but not all**, to pass through?

TOXIC

Science Chatterbox 2

5 Which kind of material **allows ALL** the **light through?**

an **opaque** material

a **translucent** material

6 Explain what a **brittle** material is

transparent

a material which will *break easily* **if it is bent**

a **flexible** material

a material which can be **burned**

8 What do we call a material which can **bend** without **breaking?**

a **STRONG** material

a **rigid** material

7 Explain what a **flammable** material is

STRONG

4 What do you call a material which will **not break or crack** unless **strong forces are used?**

3 What do you call a material which **will not bend unless** a strong force is used?

FLAMMABLE

© Chris Jones 2008

Unit 3C

Characteristics of Materials

Chatterbox 3 Level 3

PROPERTY

Unit 3C Characteristics of Materials

1 Which name is given to a material which **breaks easily** if it's **bent?**

2 What do you call a material which can be **stretched**, but will **return back** to its **shape?**

OPAQUE

Science Chatterbox 3

5 This material is a **mixture** of **different gases**

a brittle material

AIR

an elastic material

a flammable material

6 What do we call a material which is able to **burn?**

8 A material that **bends easily** is called...?

flexible

strength

HARDNESS

IRON (or mixtures containing iron - like steel)

7 A material's **resistance** to **scratching** is called its ...?

TRANSPARENT

4 A material's **resistance** to **breaking** is called its...?

3 The **only metal** which is **magnetic** is called ...?

TRANSLUCENT

Unit 3C

Characteristics of Materials

Chatterbox 4 Level 4

Unit 3C Characteristics of Materials

RESISTANCE

1 What is an **impermeable** material?

2 Why are **car tyres** made from **rubber?**

Science Chatterbox 4

PERMEABLE

5 A material that will **Not** let **heat through** easily, is called a ...?

a material which **doesn't** allow water to **pass through** (be absorbed)

because rubber is *strong, flexible* and has a good *grip*

6 Why is a **crane** made from **metal?**

THERMAL INSULATOR

metal is **rigid** and **strong**

permeable

material which **allows** water to **pass through** (be absorbed)

toxic

impermeable

8 A soil that **allows** water to **pass through** it easily is called...?

7 A material that could **poison** you if **eaten** is called.?

IMPERMEABLE

4 Explain what a **permeable** material is

3 A soil that **doesn't allow** water to **pass through** it **easily** is called ...?

STRENGTH

Unit 3C

Characteristics of Materials

Chatterbox 5 Level 4

SOFTNESS

Unit 3C Characteristics of Materials

1 Why is the rock, **slate**, used for ***roof tiles?***

2 Why is a towel **suitable** for **drying yourself** after a bath?

HARDNESS

Science Chatterbox 5

5 Why is **plastic** a good material for **raincoats?**

it is **rigid, strong** and **impermeable**

a towel is *soft, flexible* and *permeable*

6 Why is **glass** used as **material** to make **windows?**

it is **flexible, light** and **impermeable**

glass is **rigid** **strong** and ***transparent***

8 Why is **wood** a **good material** for making **matches?**

it burns easily - **FLAMMABLE**

titanium is rigid, strong and light

paper is **light** **flexible** & ***strong***

it's **impermeable**, **flexible**, and **light**

7 Why are the **pages** of a **book** made from **paper?**

© Chris Jones 2008

SCRATCHES

4 Why is a spaceship made from **titanium?**

3 Why is **plastic** used to coat the **outside** of electric cable?

RESISTANT

Unit 3C

Characteristics of Materials

Chatterbox 6 Level 4

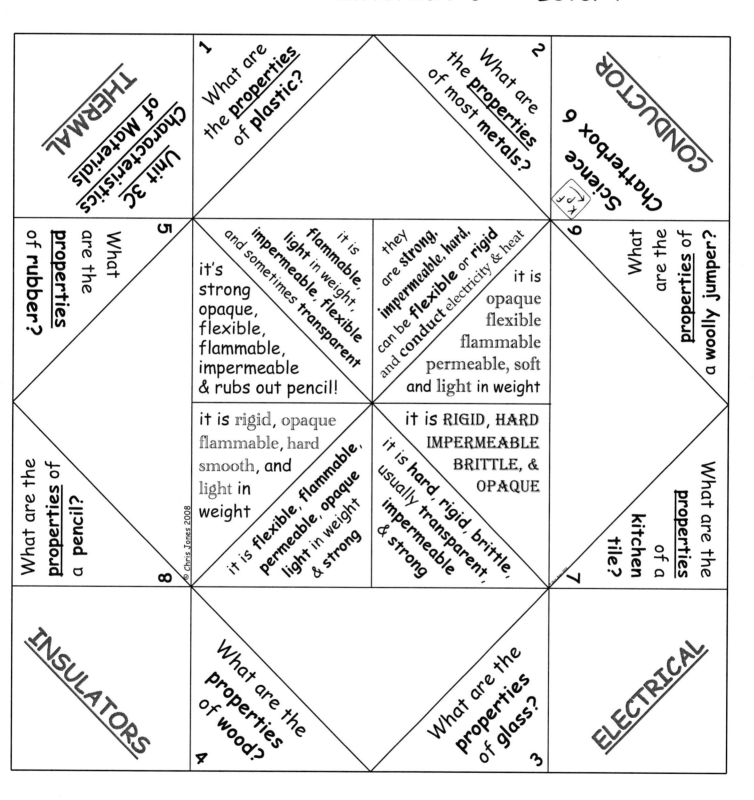

THERMAL

Unit 3C Characteristics of Materials

1 What are the **properties** of **plastic?**

2 What are the **properties** of most **metals?**

CONDUCTOR

Science Chatterbox 6

5 What are the **properties** of **rubber?**

it is **flammable, light** in weight, **impermeable, flexible** and sometimes **transparent**

it's strong opaque, flexible, flammable, impermeable & rubs out pencil!

they are **strong, impermeable, hard,** can be **flexible** or **rigid** and **conduct** electricity & heat

it is opaque flexible flammable permeable, soft and light in weight

6 What are the **properties** of a **woolly jumper?**

8 What are the **properties** of a **pencil?**

it is rigid, opaque flammable, hard smooth, and light in weight

it is **flexible, flammable, permeable, opaque light** in weight & **strong**

it is RIGID, HARD IMPERMEABLE BRITTLE, & OPAQUE

it is **hard, rigid, brittle,** usually **transparent, impermeable & strong**

7 What are the **properties** of a **kitchen tile?**

© Chris Jones 2008

INSULATORS

4 What are the **properties** of **wood?**

3 What are the **properties** of **glass?**

ELECTRICAL

Unit 3C

Characteristics of Materials

Chatterbox 7 Level 4

PERMEABILITY

Unit 3C Characteristics of Materials

1 What do we call a material which **doesn't allow** water to **pass through** (be absorbed)?

2 What do we call a material that **absorbs**, or **soaks up**, water or other liquids?

ABSORBENT

Science Chatterbox 7

5 This type of soil is fairly **impermeable**

an **impermeable** material

clay soil

a PERMEABLE material

sandy soil

6 This type of soil is **very permeable**

electrical conductor

a material which can **absorb**, or **soak up** water or other liquids

flammable

a permeable material

8 A material that **lets electricity pass through** it is called an.....?

© Chris Jones 2008

7 A material which **burns easily** is called ...?

IMPERMEABILITY

4 Explain what an **absorbent** material is

3 What do you call a material which **allows** water to **pass through** (be absorbed)?

CHARACTERISTICS

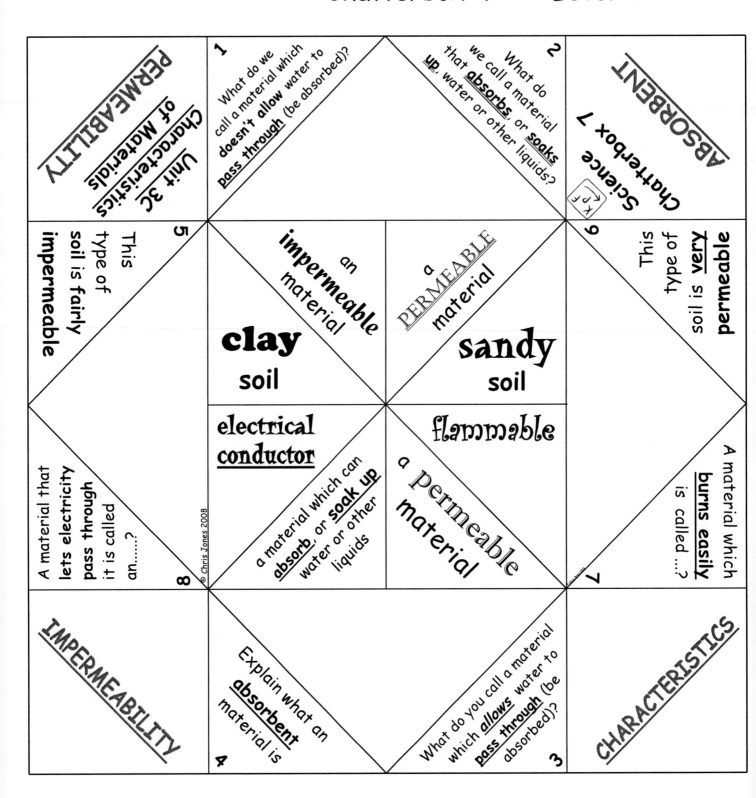

Unit 3D

Rocks and Soils

Chatterbox 1 Level 3

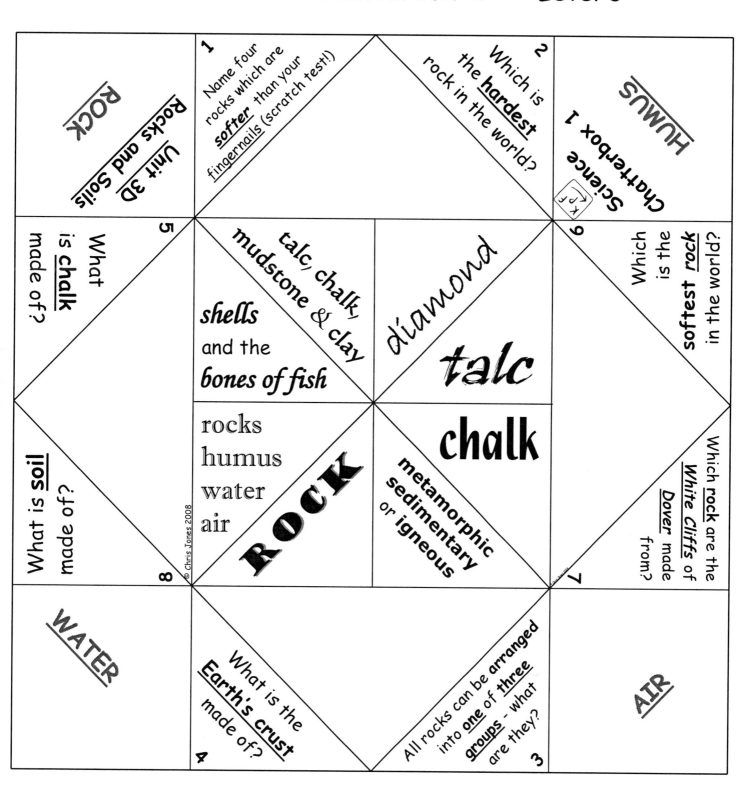

ROCK

Unit 3D
Rocks and Soils

1 Name four rocks which are ***softer*** than your fingernails (scratch test!)

2 Which is the **hardest** rock in the world?

HUMUS

Science Chatterbox 1

5 What is **chalk** made of?

talc, chalk, mudstone & clay

shells and the ***bones of fish***

diamond

talc

6 Which is the **softest rock** in the world?

What is **soil** made of?

rocks
humus
water
air

ROCK

chalk

metamorphic sedimentary or **igneous**

Which **rock** are the ***White Cliffs*** of ***Dover*** made from? 7

© Chris Jones 2008

8

WATER

4 What is the **Earth's crust** made of?

3 All rocks can be **arranged** into **one** of **three groups** - what are they?

AIR

Unit 3D

Rocks and Soils

Chatterbox 2 Level 3

CKALKY

Unit 3D Rocks and Soils

PEAT

Science Chatterbox 2

SANDY

SOILS

1 Which **states of matter** are soils made from?

2 What did children living in Victorian Times use to **write with**, in their schools?

3 Where is the **driest** place on Earth?

4 Why is it possible to **write** with **chalk?**

5 What is the favoured **rock** used to **carve** sculptures?

6 What is the **humus** in the **soil** made from?

7 Which **rock** is **glass** made from?

8 Which **rock** is used to make **bricks?**

gas (air), **liquid** (water) & **solids** (rock and humus)

they used **slate-boards** - they had a metal 'pen' which **scratched** the slate

dead and **decaying** plants & animals

marble

clay - which is baked hard in a kiln

because chalk is **soft**, it comes away easily - leaving a mark

sand

the **Atacama Desert** - only half a millimetre of rain every year!!

Unit 3D

Rocks and Soils

Chatterbox 3 Level 4

SANDSTONE

Unit 3D Rocks and Soils

1 How do **different** soils **vary** in **character?**

2 What are the **characteristics** of **chalky soil?**

CHALK

Science Chatterbox 3

5 Name three examples of **metamorphic rock**

the **main differences DEPEND** on the **TYPE** of **rock** and the **AMOUNT** of **humus & water** they contain

slate
marble
quartz

there is enough **water & humus** to *support growth*, lots of **chalk** and lots of **air spaces**, making it **permeable**

chalk, mudstone, limestone, clay, sandstone

6 Name five examples of **sedimentary rock**

8 What does **permeable** mean?

permeable means - to allow water or other liquids to pass through

lots of **rock** in the form of sand, lots of **air spaces**, **hardly any water** or **humus**. Very **permeable**

iron pyrite, granite, basalt.

it's **dark coloured**, contains **lots of humus & water** but not so much **rock** and **air**

7 Give 3 examples of **igneous rock**

SEDIMENTARY

4 What are the **characteristics** of **sandy soil?**

3 What are the **characteristics** of **peat soil?**

LIMESTONE

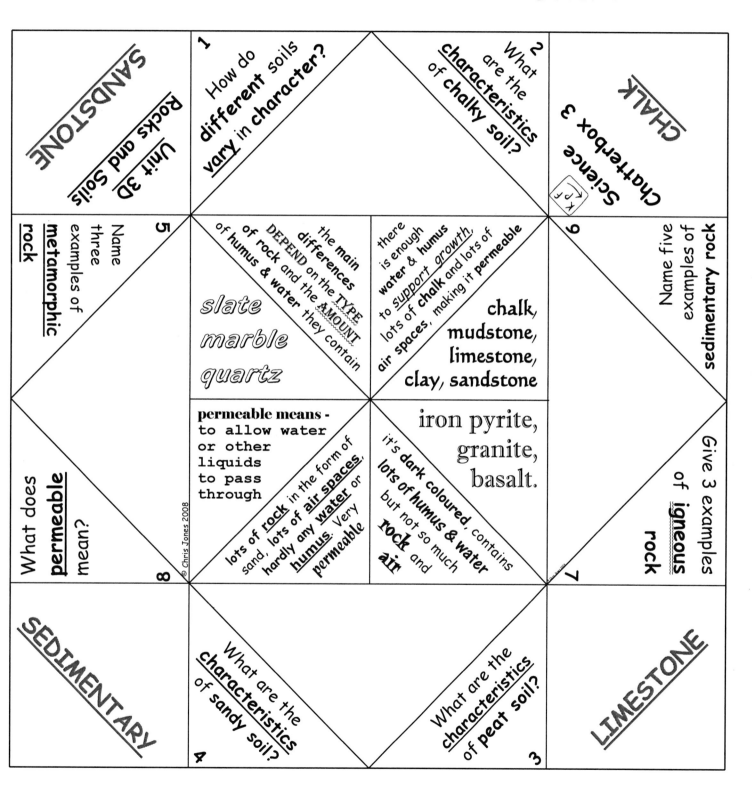

Unit 3D

Rocks and Soils

Chatterbox 4 Level 4

QUARTZ

Unit 3D Rocks and Soils

1 How does the **size** of **rock particles effect** the *flow of water* through a soil sample?

2 Why is **slate** often **used** for **roof tiles?**

MARBLE

Science Chatterbox 4

5 What do we call a rock that **allows water** to **pass through?**

the **larger** the **rock particles**, the **faster water will go through** the soil (there are larger air spaces)

permeable

it can be **cut** into **thin sections**, **it's rigid**, **strong** and **IMPERMEABLE**

impermeable

6 What do we call rock that **doesn't allow** any water to **pass through?**

8 What are the **characteristics** of **loam soil?**

it **holds water** well, contains **lots** of **humus** and **air** but not so much **rock**

it contains lots of air spaces making it very permeable **- rainwater soaks through it quickly**

because it's ***extremely hard*** and ***will not wear away*** easily

pumice stone - this was 'frothy' lava, that cooled **very fast**, **trapping the air bubbles inside**

7 Why is **granite** sometimes used for the **floors** and **steps** of buildings?

METAMORPHIC

4 Why is **sandy soil** usually **very dry?**

3 What is the **only rock** that can **float?**

SLATE

Unit 3D

Rocks and Soils

Chatterbox 5 Level 4

BASALT Unit 3D Rocks and Soils	1 Describe the **kind of soil** **worms might prefer**	2 Why is **clay soil not so good** for growing plants?	GRANITE Science Chatterbox 5
5 If you see a **200 foot tall tree**, what does that **tell you** about the **soil** it's growing in?	soils that contain **water**, enough **air** to breath and enough decaying **humus** to feed on **it must be deep**, because tall trees need a **deep** root system to **support them**	clay is made of **tiny particles**, so there are **few air spaces**, making it hard for roots to grow -and worms to live! **granite** is **igneous** the others are **metamorphic**	6 Which is the *odd one out*; - **slate marble, granite?**
8 On a beach, which **kind of rock** do you find **rock pools** formed from?	an ***impermeable rock***, which prevents the water from draining away the scratch test -rub them together - whichever has a scratch is the softest	they're sedimentary & PERMEABLE **quartz** is impermeable and metamorphic -the others are **permeable** and **sedimentary** -any others?	7 What do these rocks have in common - **mudstone sandstone chalk?**
IRON PYRITE	4 How could you **test** which is the **hardest rock** - ***limestone*** or ***granite?***	3 Which is the odd one out; **chalk, sandstone** or **quartz?**	IGNEOUS

Unit 3D

Rocks and Soils

Chatterbox 6 Level 5

MUDSTONE

Unit 3D Rocks and Soils

1 What is, and how is, **marble formed?**

2 What is, and how is, **limestone formed?**

PERMEABLE

Science Chatterbox 6

5 How would you **separate** the **different sized** rocks and particles in soil?

it's **metamorphic** formed when **limestone is heated and compressed**. It started off as **chalk** (shells and fish bones)

by using **DIFFERENT SIZED SIEVES**

it's a metamorphic **rock**, formed when **layers of chalk were compressed under enormous pressure**

new products are being made - so it's an **irreversible change**

6 When **vinegar** is dropped onto **chalk** - *bubbles form*. Which **type of change** is happening?

8 Why is marble **impermeable?**

because it was formed at **high pressures** -it is **completely solid** without **any air spaces**

Sedimetary rocks - there are gaps between the rock particles - **allowing water to pass through**

marble or **limestone** both of these are ***dissolved*** by **acids** (even very weak ones)

because there are **air spaces between** the sand grains **allowing** water to **pass through** these spaces

7 A statue in a **polluted** city with **acid rain** is very **corroded**. Which rock could it be made from?

IMPERMEABLE

4 Which kind of rocks are usually **permeable?**

3 Why is **sandstone permeable?**

SAND

Unit 3D

Rocks and Soils

Chatterbox 7 Level 5

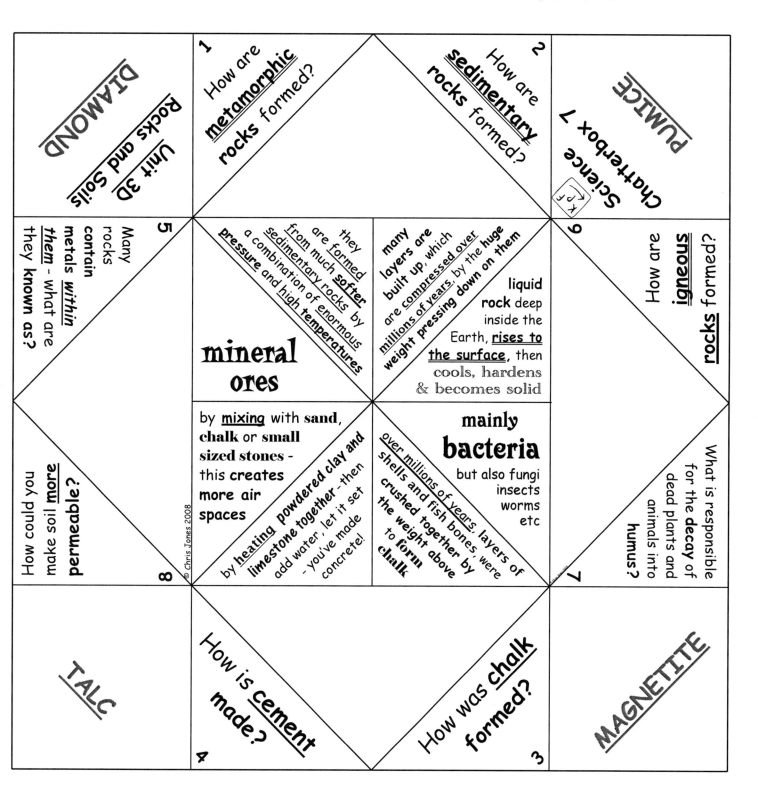

DIAMOND

Unit 3D Rocks and Soils

1 How are **metamorphic rocks** formed?

2 How are **sedimentary rocks** formed?

PUMICE

Science Chatterbox 7

5 Many rocks **contain metals *within them*** - what are they **known as?**

they are formed from much **softer** sedimentary rocks by a combination of enormous **pressure** and high **temperatures**

mineral ores

many layers are built up, which are compressed over millions of years, by the **huge weight pressing down on them**

liquid rock deep inside the Earth, **rises to the surface**, then cools, hardens & becomes solid

6 How are **igneous rocks** formed?

8 How could you make soil **more permeable?**

by mixing with **sand**, **chalk** or **small sized stones** - this **creates more air spaces**

by **heating powdered clay and limestone together** - then add water, let it set - you've made concrete!

over millions of years, layers of shells and fish bones, were **crushed together by the weight above** to **form chalk**

mainly bacteria but also fungi insects worms etc

7 What is responsible for the **decay** of dead plants and animals into **humus?**

TALC

4 How is **cement** made?

3 How was **chalk** formed?

MAGNETITE

Unit 3E

Magnets and Springs

Chatterbox 1 Level 3

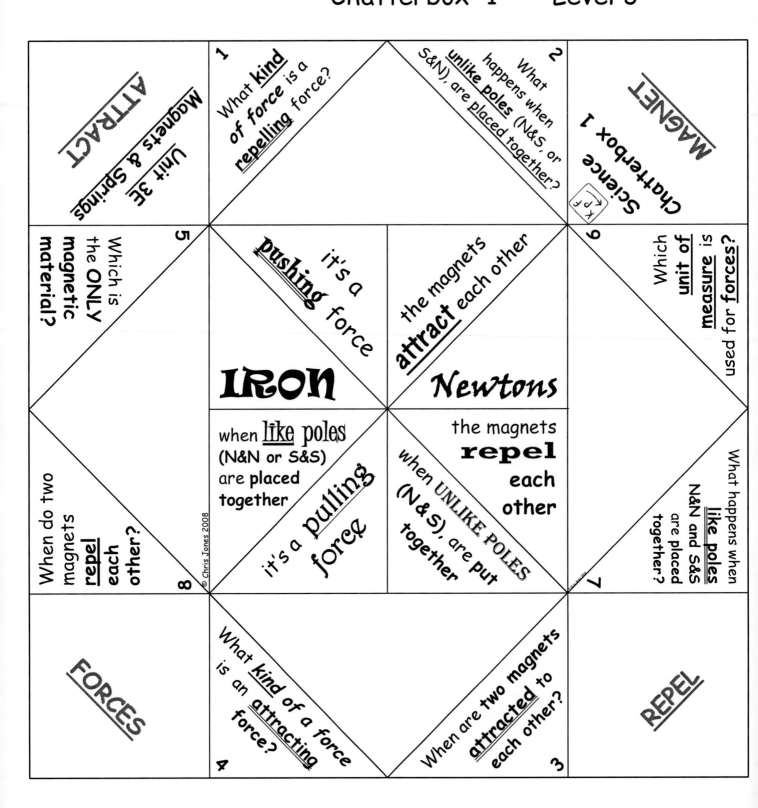

Unit 3E
Magnets & Springs

ATTRACT

1 What **kind of force** is a **repelling** force?

2 What happens when **unlike poles** (N&S, or S&N), are placed together?

Science Chatterbox 1

MAGNET

5 Which is the **ONLY magnetic material?**

it's a **pushing** force

the magnets **attract** each other

6 Which **unit of measure** is used for **forces?**

IRON

Newtons

8 When do two magnets **repel** each other?

when **like poles** (N&N or S&S) are placed together

it's a **pulling force**

the magnets **repel** each other

when **UNLIKE POLES** (N&S), are put together

7 What happens when **like poles** N&N and S&S are placed together?

© Chris Jones 2008

FORCES

4 What **kind of a force** is an **attracting** force?

3 When are **two magnets attracted** to each other?

REPEL

Unit 3E

Magnets and Springs

Chatterbox 2   Level 3

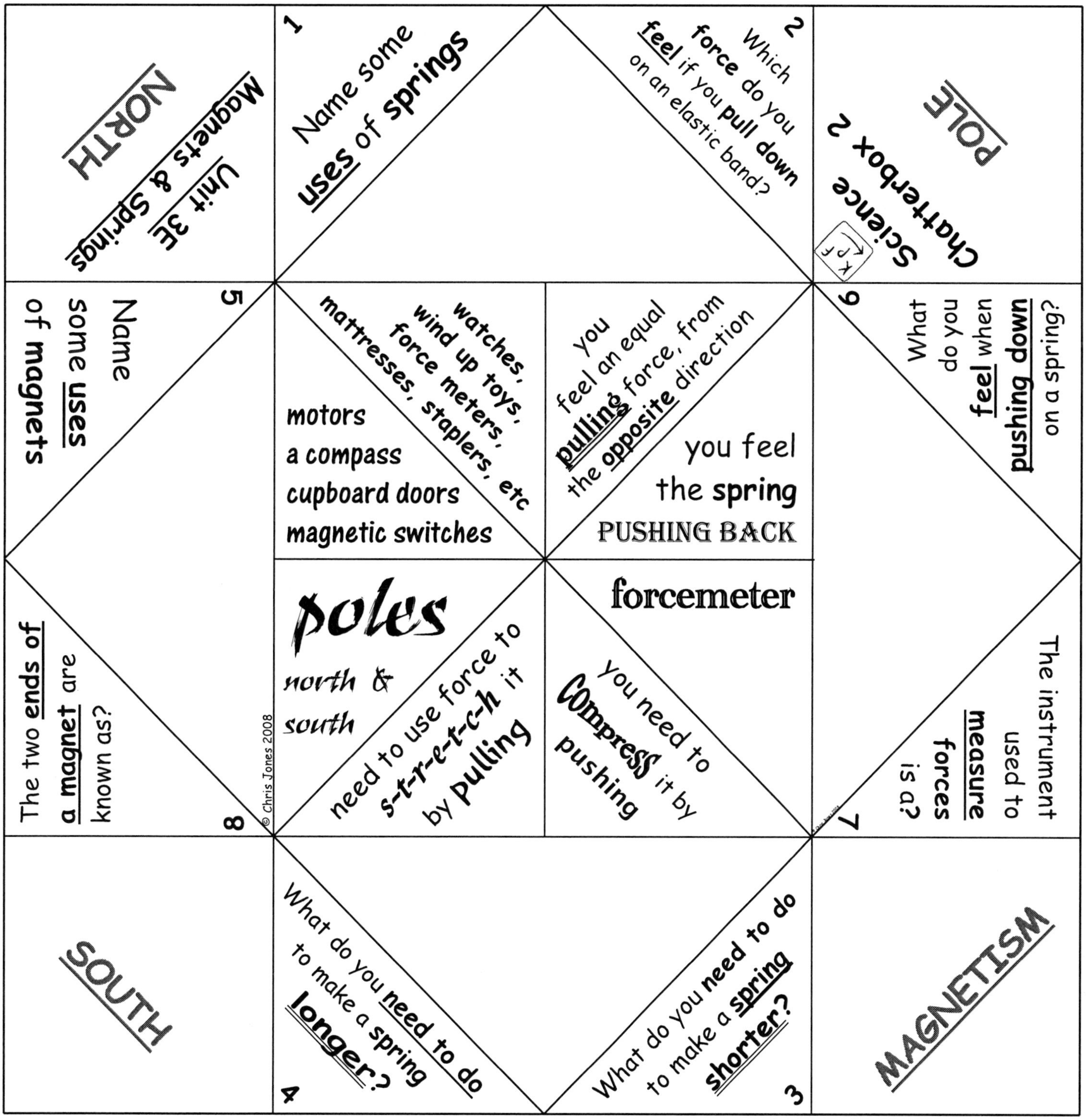
NORTH
Magnets & Springs
Unit 3E
1
Name some uses of springs
2
Which force do you feel if you pull down on an elastic band?
POLE
Science Chatterbox 2
5
Name some uses of magnets
watches, wind up toys, force meters, mattresses, staplers, etc
motors
a compass
cupboard doors
magnetic switches
you feel an equal pulling force, from the opposite direction
you feel the spring PUSHING BACK
6
What do you feel when pushing down on a spring?
8
The two ends of a magnet are known as?
poles
north & south
need to use force to s-t-r-e-t-c-h it by pulling
forcemeter
You need to Compress it by pushing
© Chris Jones 2008
7
The instrument used to measure forces is a?
SOUTH
4
What do you need to do to make a spring longer?
3
What do you need to do to make a spring shorter?
MAGNETISM

Unit 3E

Magnets and Springs

Chatterbox 3 Level 4

STRETCH

Unit 3E Magnets & Springs

1 Why does a *Jack in the Box* jump out as soon as the box is opened?

2 What is **magnetism?**

SPRING

Science Chatterbox 3

5 Why are some metals **not attracted** to magnets?

because it is attached to a spring which has been compressed

an **invisible force** that **ATTRACTS iron or metals containing iron**

6 Material **returning** to its **original shape** after being pulled, squashed or twisted, is called?

because they **don't contain IRON**

elastic

8 Materials which are **attracted** to **magnets** are said to be?

magnetic

it is **PUSHING them apart**

the **needle** is a **magnet** other **materials** are **non-magnetic** - so they don't affect the needle

an iron nail **does not** have ***elastic*** properties

7 Which **kind** of **materials** is a **compass** made from?

NEWTONS

4 How is the **force acting** if two magnets **repel each other?**

3 Which is the odd one out; a balloon, an iron nail, a rubber band, a trampoline?

FORCEMETER

Unit 3E

Magnets and Springs

Chatterbox 4 Level 4

PULLING

Unit 3E Magnets & Springs

1 How does the **amount** of **force** on a spring **affect** the **amount** it stretches?

2 How does the **strength** of a **magnet**, **affect** its **attraction to iron?**

PUSHING

Science Chatterbox 4

5 What is a **spring balance?**

the **GREATER** the **force**, the **GREATER** the **amount** of **S-T-R-E-T-C-H**

a **device** which **uses** a **spring to measure a force** e.g. a forcemeter

the **stronger** the magnet, the **greater the force of attraction**

a **pulling force** which causes objects to **have weight**

6 What is **gravity?**

8 We call a magnet **powered** by **electricity** an.....?

electro-magnet

the **further** a catapult is **stretched** the **greater the distance** an **object is thrown**

because it **contains iron**

the **stronger** the magnet, the **greater** the **number of paperclips** it **can hold**

7 Why does **steel attract** to **magnets?**

© Chris Jones 2008

FIELD

4 What **effect** does the **amount** a catapult is **stretched**, have on the **distance** an object is **thrown?**

3 How does a magnet's **strength effect** the **number of paperclips** it can hold?

IRON

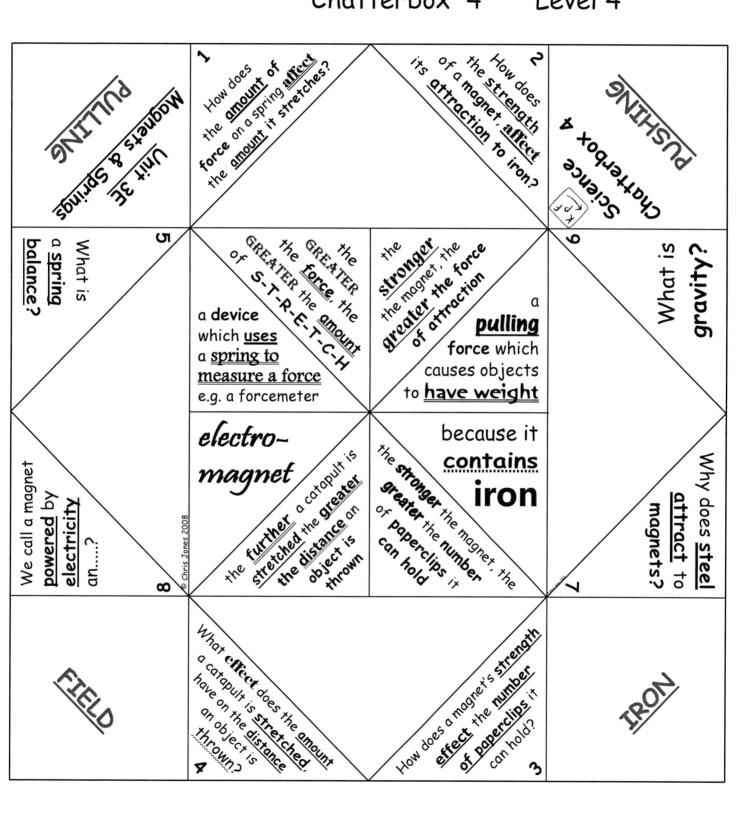

Unit 3E

Magnets and Springs

Chatterbox 5 Level 5

COMPASS

Unit 3E Magnets & Springs

1 Explain why a compass **always points north?**

2 How could an **electromagnet** be made in the classroom?

MAGNETIC

Science Chatterbox 5

5 How is it possible to '**SEE**' the **magnetic field** of a magnet?

the **needle is a magnet** - so the marked end is **always attracted towards** the real North Pole

sprinkle iron filings onto a piece of paper placed over a magnet

coil a wire from a circuit around an iron nail - when **the current is turned on - it becomes an electromagnet**

the AREA AROUND A MAGNET in which the magnetic force has an effect

6 What is a **magnetic field?**

8 If the **coils of a spring** are **pulled apart**, then let go - **how is the force acting?**

the **force pulls towards the centre** of the spring

because **gravity** is so INCREDIBLY POWERFUL **- not even light can escape!**

STEEL because it's the only **magnetic metal** -can you think of more?

the Earth is **much larger than the Moon**, so its *gravity* is **much greater**

7 Which is the **odd one out**; gold, aluminium, steel or copper?

© Chris Jones 2008

NEWTON

4 Why is a '**black hole**' in space, so **black?**

3 **Gravity** on Earth is **6 times stronger** than **gravity on the Moon**. Explain

ELECTROMAGNET

Unit 3F

Light and Shadow

Chatterbox 1 Level 3

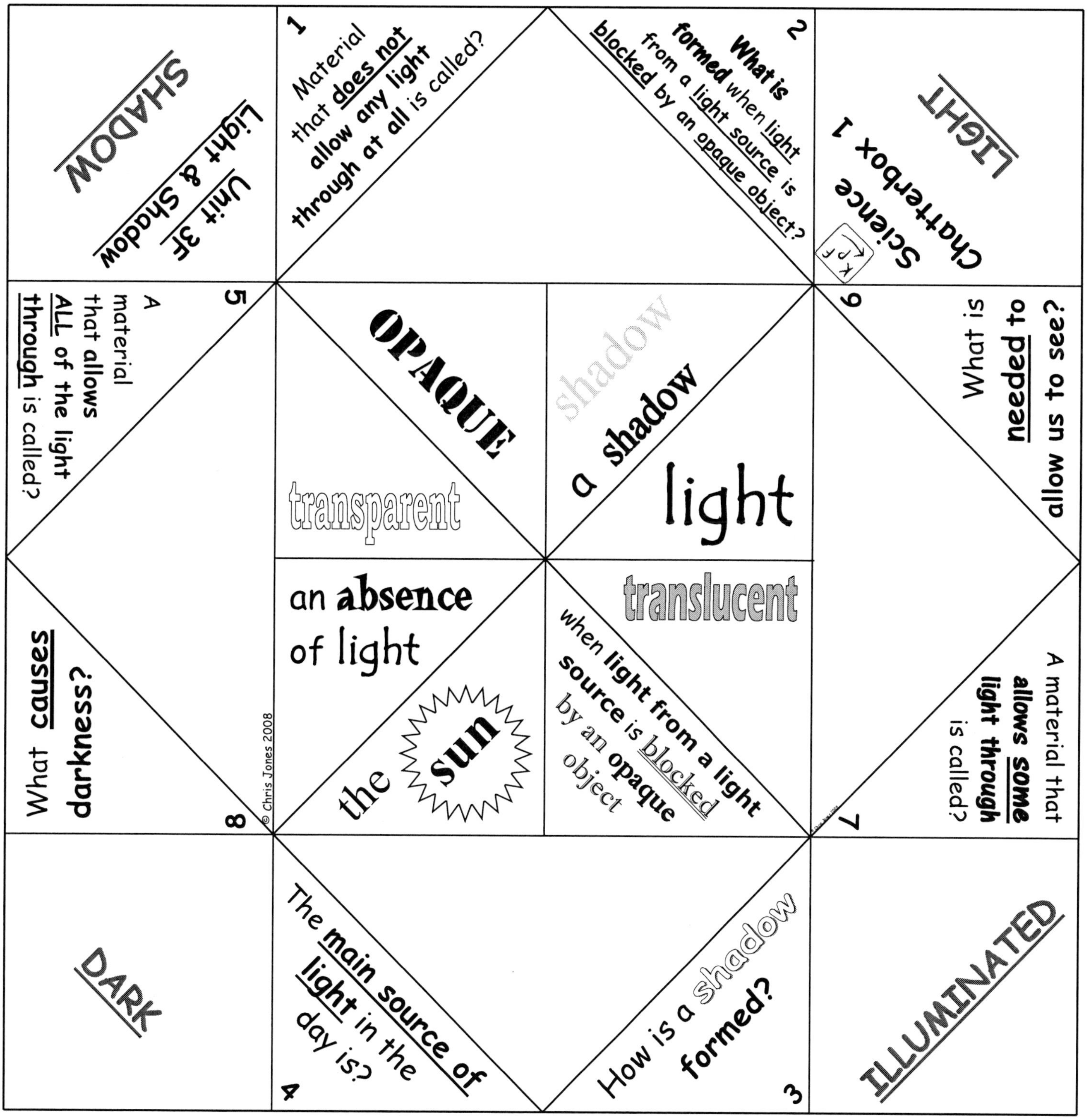

Unit 3F

Light and Shadow

Chatterbox 2 Level 3

IMAGE

Unit 3F
Light & Shadow

1
How is a **shadow's shape** **similar** to the **object that is making it?**

2
How does **shadow length change** from **sunrise to midday?**

REFLECT

Science Chatterbox 2

KPF

5
The **picture formed in a mirror** is called?

the shadow is the **same shape**, but not always the **same size**

an IMAGE or REFLECTION

shadow length gets **shorter**

shadow length gets **longer**

6
How does **shadow length change**, from **midday to sunset?**

All materials that **reflect light** are said to be?

8

© Chris Jones 2008

reflective

a **shadow**

transparent

because it's impermeable, rigid, and transparent to allow light through

What **kind of material** is **glass?**

7

REFLECTION

The **area of darkness formed, when an object blocks light, is?**

4

Why is **glass** a **good material** for **windows?**

3

REFLECTIVE

Unit 3F

Light and Shadow

Chatterbox 3 Level 4

MATERIAL

Unit 3F Light & Shadow

1 How do we **see an object** in a room?

2 Why does the **length of a shadow change** during the day?

OPAQUE

Science Chatterbox 3

5 At which time of day are **shadows shortest?**

light from a **light source**, **reflects** off an object, in **straight lines**, directly into our eyes

about MIDDAY when the Sun is at its HIGHEST

because the Sun is at **different positions** during the day - so sunlight hits objects at different angles

very fast & in straight → **lines**

6 How does **light travel?**

8 Why does the Sun **appear** to **move across the sky?**

because the Earth is ***rotating on its axis***

the Sun **sets** in the WEST

the Sun **rises** in the *EAST*

NO! we only see the Moon because **sunlight** is **reflecting** off it

7 Where does the **Sun rise?**

© Chris Jones 2008

TRANSLUCENT

4 Where does the **Sun set?**

3 Is the Moon a **light source?**

TRANSPARENT

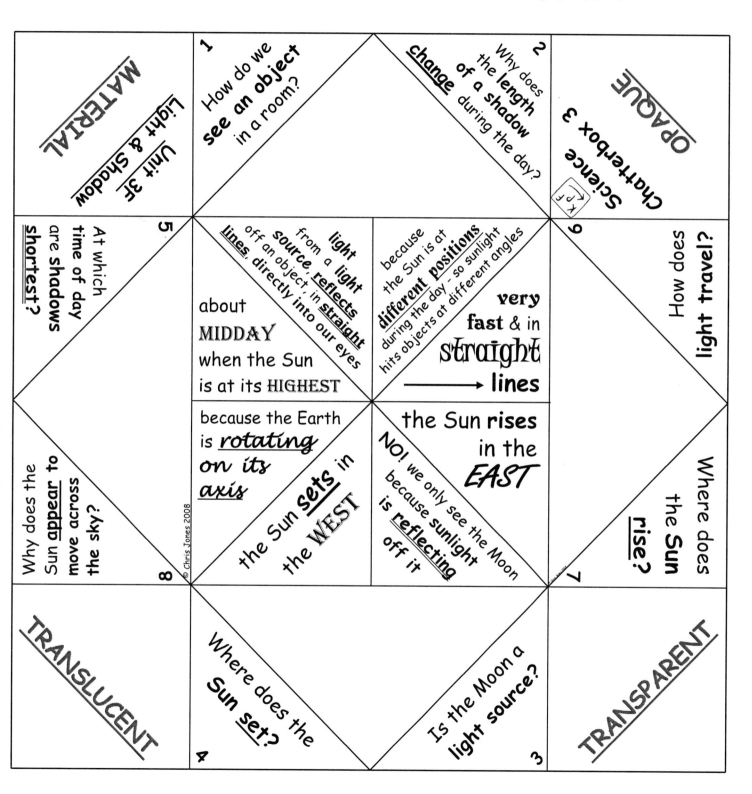

Unit 3F

Light and Shadow

Chatterbox 4 Level 4

EARTH

Light & Shadow Unit 3F

1 How does the **distance** of a light source **affect** the **size of the shadow?**

2 How does the **distance** of an **object from a light source, AFFECT the size of its shadow?**

SUN

Science Chatterbox 4

5 How does the **height** of the Sun, affect the **length of a shadow?**

the further away the light source, the **smaller the shadow**

the FURTHER AWAY the **object is**, the SMALLER ITS SHADOW

6 How **long** does the Earth **take** to **revolve once on its axis?**

the HIGHER the **Sun**, the SHORTER the **shadow**

one day- 24 hours

because they are ***able to*** **reflect more light**

mid-summers day **June 21st** -the **longest** day

8 Why do **metals** often **look** so **shiny?**

because **not all the light can get through** - so usually you get a 'lighter' shadow

if it is reflected by using a mirror for example

7 On **which day** does the **Sun** reach its **highest point** each year?

ROTATING

4 Why can a **translucent material make a shadow?**

3 What is the **only way** a **beam of light** can **travel around corners?**

AXIS

Unit 3F

Light and Shadow

Chatterbox 5 Level 4

REFLECT

Unit 3F
Light & Shadow

MIRROR

Science
Chatterbox 5

EAST

SUNRISE

1 How is a **ray of light** represented in diagrams?

2 Which is the **odd one out**; a safety jacket, the Moon, a TV, a mirror?

3 Which is the **odd one out**; ***a mirror, a window, a whiteboard or a 10p coin?***

4 Why does the Moon **appear** to **change shape** during each month?

5 What time is it, on the Earth **facing** the Sun?

6 What **is formed** when an object blocks light from a light source?

7 What time is it on the part of the Earth **facing away from** the Sun?

8 What has to **reflect off your face**, to allow you to see yourself in a mirror?

with a **straight arrow**, pointing in the **direction the light travels**

the TV, it is the only **light source**

day-time

a shadow

rays of light because **different amounts** are in **shadow**

night-time

the window is ***transparent*** the others are **opaque**

© Chris Jones 2008

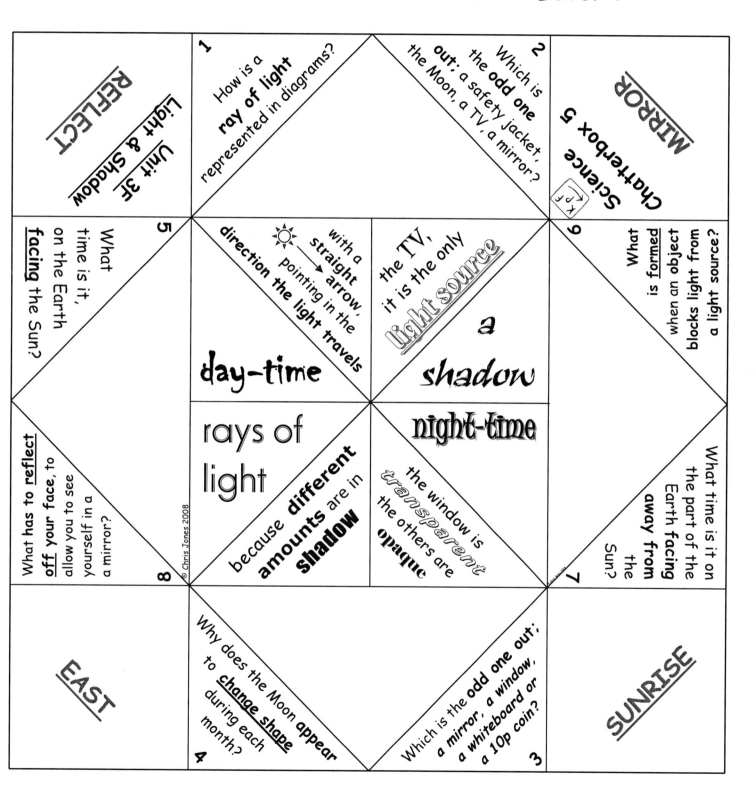

Unit 3F

Light and Shadow

Chatterbox 6 Level 5

WEST

Unit 3F Light & Shadow

SUNSET

Science Chatterbox 6

LONGER

SHADOWS

1 Name some **natural** light sources

candles, lightning, fires, stars, fireflies, etc.

2 Why do most fabrics **allow** a **bit** of light through?

they are made of fibres, so they **contain** many **air spaces**, so **some** light is usually able to get through

3 **How far away** is the **Sun** from the **Earth?**

93,000,000 miles

93 million miles

4 Name **two types of light** that humans can't see

infra red rays and **X rays**

5 How **long** does it take light from the Sun **to reach us?**

about **8½ minutes**!!

6 How **fast** does **light travel?**

300,000 km per second

or - **186,000** miles per second

7 A device that uses **mirrors** to **look around corners** is called a ...?

periscope

8 Name some **artificial** light sources

car headlights
streetlights
torches
etc.

Unit 4A

Moving and Growing

Chatterbox 1   Level 3

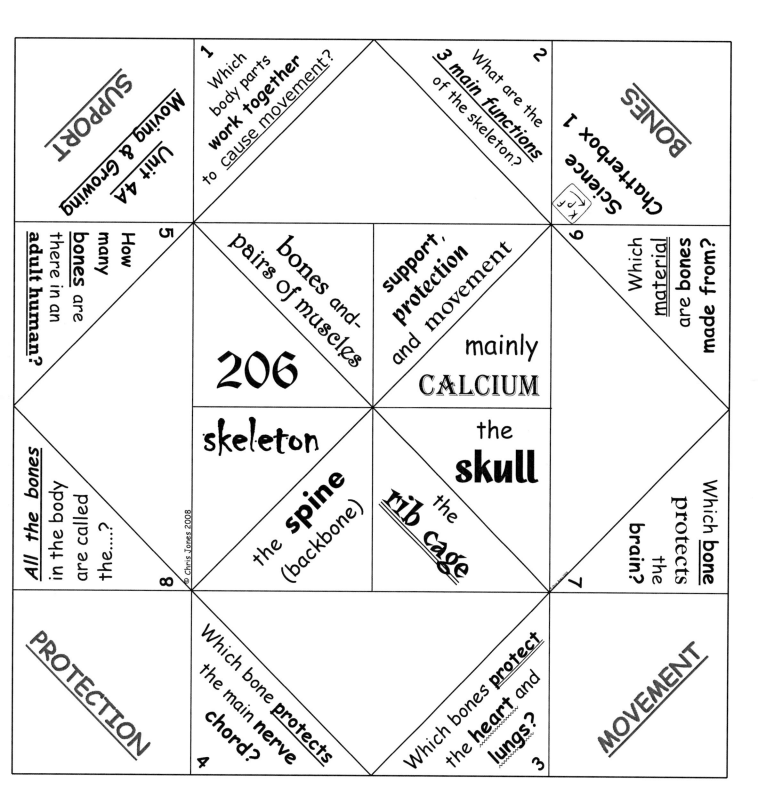

SUPPORT

Moving & Growing Unit 4A

1 Which body parts **work together** to cause movement?

2 What are the **3 main functions** of the skeleton?

Science Chatterbox 1

BONES

5 How many **bones** are there in an **adult human?**

bones and pairs of muscles

206

skeleton

support, protection and movement

mainly

CALCIUM

6 Which **material** are **bones made from?**

All the bones in the body are called the.....?

the **spine** (backbone)

the **rib cage**

the **skull**

Which **bone** protects the **brain?**

© Chris Jones 2008

PROTECTION

8

Which bone **protects** the main **nerve chord?**

4

Which bones **protect** the **heart** and **lungs?**

3

MOVEMENT

7

© Chris Jones 2008

Unit 4A

Moving and Growing

Chatterbox 2 Level 3

SKULL

Moving & Growing Unit 4A

1 What are the **muscles** on the **upper arm** called?

2 Which is the **largest bone** in the human body?

SKELETON

Science Chatterbox 2

5 What is your **pulse?**

the **biceps** and **triceps**

the **femur** (thigh bone)

6 Which **food group** provides a good **calcium** source?

your **heart beat**

DAIRY PRODUCE

about 74 - 78 **beats per minute**

to **pump blood** around the body

8 What is the **average** resting pulse rate?

the **pulse rate**

the HEART

7 What is the **function** of the **heart?**

BACKBONE

4 What is the scientific term for how many times the **heart beats a minute?**

3 Which is the MOST **important muscle** in the body?

VERTEBRAE

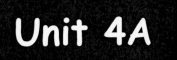

Unit 4A

Moving and Growing

Chatterbox 3 Level 3

PULSE

Unit 4A
Moving & Growing

1 What **happens** to the bones in your body as you **grow?**

2 Which **special picture** does a doctor take to **look at your bones?**

HEART

Science
Chatterbox 3

5 A **balanced diet** contains foods from different ..... ?

the bones
get bigger

an
X-ray

6 Which is the **largest muscle** in the body?

food
groups

your bum!!
the
gluteus maximus

the
brain

PROTEIN

8 Which organ **controls movement?**

you only need **14 muscles** to **smile** - you need **22 muscles** to **frown!**

carbohydrate

7 Which **food type** is good for **building muscles?**

© Chris Jones 2008

EXERCISE

4 Is it easier to **smile** ☺ or **frown** ☹ ?

3 What do we call the **energy food** for **exercise?**

CARBOHYDRATE

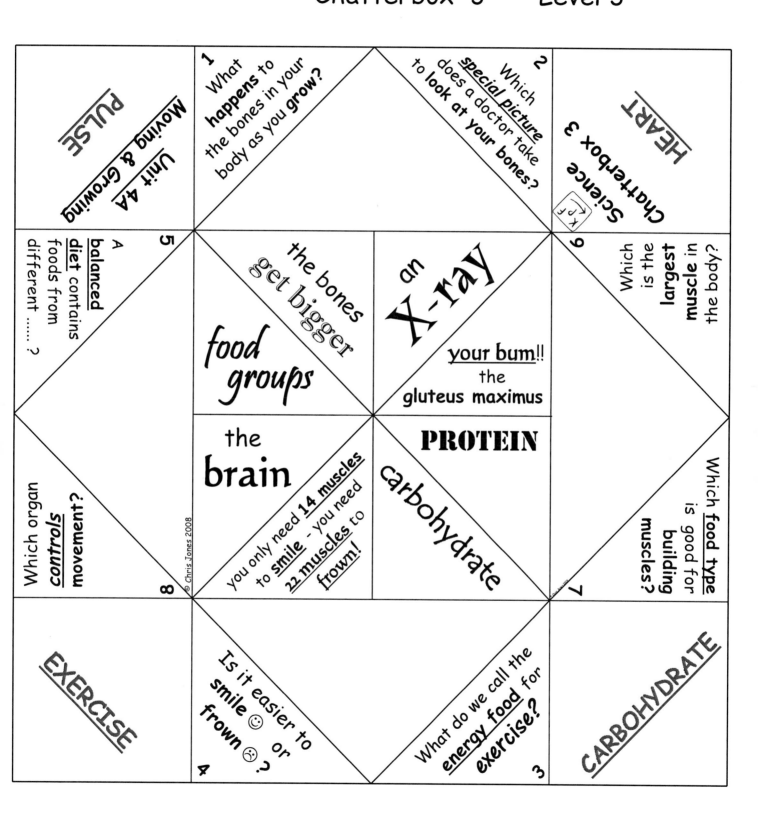

Unit 4A

Moving and Growing

Chatterbox 4 Level 4

PAIRS

Unit 4A
Moving & Growing

1 How does the **type of exercise** you do, **affect the pulse rate?**

2 Explain how you **straighten** your arm

MUSCLE

Science Chatterbox 4

5 What do **muscles need** to work?

the **HARDER** (more vigorous) the **EXERCISE**, then the **higher the pulse rate**

they need **oxygen** and **energy** (sugar)

the **triceps** muscle **contracts** (**biceps relaxes**) pulling your lower arm away from you

the **longer** the femur bone, the **taller** someone is

6 How does the **length** of **the femur** bone **affect** the **height** of someone?

8 How do you **scratch** your **nose?**

the **bicepts muscle contracts**, pulling your hand towards your nose!! (one finger sticking out, of course)

the **bicepts muscle contracts**, **pulling** the lower arm bone **towards** you

sweating

it's a way of **cooling** - when sweat evaporates, the **skin cools down**

7 A mechanism for **keeping cool during exercise** is by?

RELAX

4 Explain how you **bend** your arm

3 Why does the body **sweat** when you **exercise?**

CONTRACT

Unit 4A

Moving and Growing

Chatterbox 5 Level 4

BICEPTS

Moving & Growing Unit 4A

1 Why does **breathing rate** *increase* during exercise?

2 Why does the **heart rate** *increase* during exercise?

TRICEPTS

Science Chatterbox 5

5 What **attaches bones to bones?**

because the **muscles** need more oxygen

ligaments

because the **muscles** NEED MORE BLOOD (containing oxygen and sugar)

hinge joints

6 Which **type of joints** are the elbows & knees?

8 What **attaches muscles to bones?**

tendons

it pulls bones towards it by **contracting** (becoming short and fat)

COMPOUND JOINTS

a **ball and socket joint**

7 Which **type of joint** are the **wrist** and **ankle?**

© Chris Jones 2008

ABDOMINAL

4 How does a **muscle** work?

3 Which **type of joint** LINKS the *arm to the shoulder* and the *leg to the body?*

GLUTEUS MAXIMUS

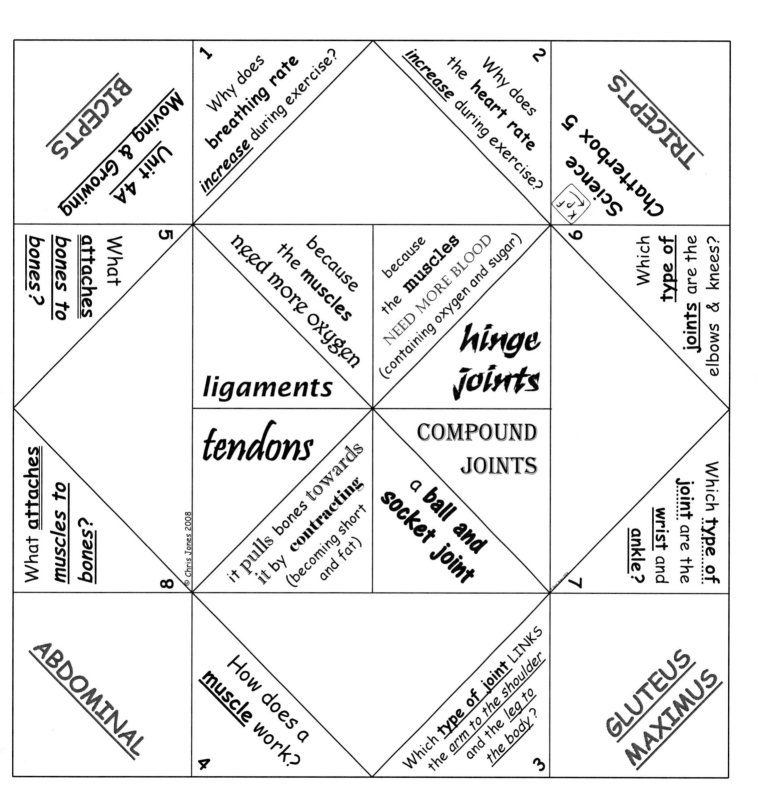

Unit 4A

Moving and Growing

Chatterbox 6 Level 4

JOINTS

Moving & Growing

Unit 4A

1 We **belong** to a ***group of animals*** called?

2 What are the **main effects** of ***exercise on the body?***

Science Chatterbox 6

COMPOUND

5 How can muscles be **strengthened?**

mammals

by **exercising**

increased breathing rate, **heart** rate and body **temperature**. The body will be **sweating** - and you feel good!

vertebrae

6 The small bones that **link together** to form the **spine** are called ..?

8 The life **process** of **becoming bigger** is known as?

© Chris Jones 2008

growth

the **cruciate ligaments**

a **key**

hammer, anvil and stirrup (in the ear)

7 We can **identify living things** by **using *what?***

HINGE

4 What are the **ligaments** in the **knee** that **foot-ballers often damage?**

3 Which are the **three smallest bones** in the body?

SOCKET

Unit 4A

Moving and Growing

Chatterbox 7 Level 5

TENDON

Unit 4A
Moving & Growing

1 The muscles **around our stomach** are called ...?

2 How are a bird's bones **adapted for flight?**

LIGAMENT

Science Chatterbox 7

5 What **degree** of **movement** does a **hinge joint allow?**

the abdominal muscles

(e.g. the knee, and elbow)

180^0

they're *hollow* to **reduce weight** to make flying easier

carbon dioxide (CO_2)

6 Which **gas** do muscles **produce** when they are **working?**

8 What is the scientific name for the **foot bones?**

metatarsals
(footballers can sometimes break them!)

360^0
(e.g. the shoulder)

© Chris Jones 2008

vertebrates

invertebrates

7 What do you call animals **with backbones?**

INVERTEBRATES

4 What **degree of movement** does a ball and socket joint allow?

3 What do you call animals **without** backbones?

VERTEBRATES

Unit 4B

Habitats

Chatterbox 1   Level 3

HUMUS

Unit 4B Habitats

1 What is the **green plant** at the ***start*** of a ***food chain*** called?

2 **Living things** are classified as plant or animal, name nine **examples of animals**

ROCK

Science Chatterbox 1

5 How are the **feeding systems** in a **habitat** REPRESENTED?

the *producer*

by using a **food chain**

bears birds, bees, bats, worms, fish, moths, lions, crocodiles

a **green plant**

6 Which living thing do **all food chains** begin with?

What is **soil** made from?

rock
humus
water
air

a **food chain**

the **Sun**

seaweed, trees, moss, dandelion, grass, mushrooms, sunflower

What is the **source** of **ALL** the Earth's energy?

7

8

© Chris Jones 2008

WATER

4 **grass → rabbit → fox** What is this an example of?

3 Living things are **plants** or **animals**, ***name seven examples of plants***

AIR

Unit 4B

Habitats

Chatterbox 2 Level 3

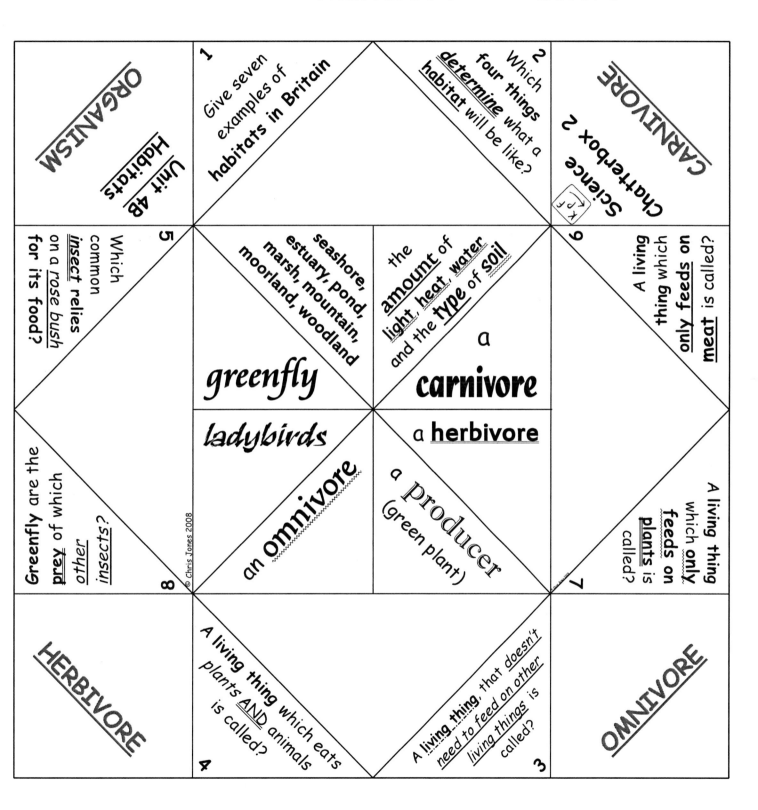

ORGANISM

Unit 4B Habitats

1 Give seven examples of **habitats in Britain**

2 Which **four things determine** what a **habitat** will be like?

CARNIVORE

Science Chatterbox 2

5 Which common **insect relies** on a *rose bush* **for its food?**

seashore, estuary, pond, marsh, mountain, moorland, woodland

the **amount** of **light**, **heat**, **water** and the **type** of **soil**

6 A living thing which **only feeds on meat** is called?

greenfly

a **carnivore**

ladybirds

a **herbivore**

8 **Greenfly** are the **prey** of which *other insects?*

an **omnivore**

a producer (green plant)

7 A living thing which **only feeds on plants** is called?

© Chris Jones 2008

HERBIVORE

4 A **living thing** which eats *plants* AND animals is called?

3 A **living thing**, that *doesn't need to feed on other living things* is called?

OMNIVORE

Unit 4B

Habitats

Chatterbox 3 Level 4

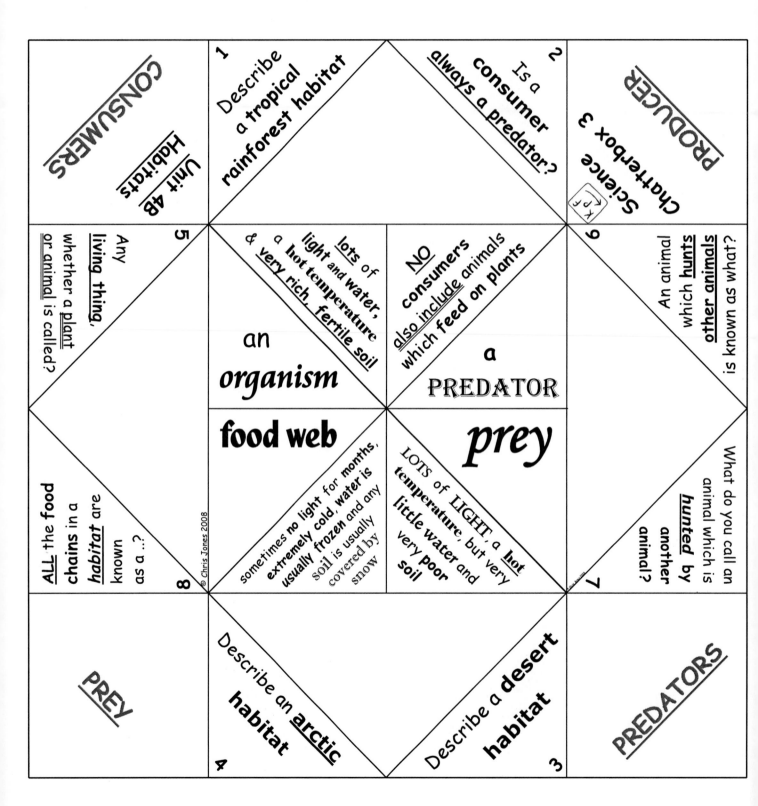

CONSUMERS

Unit 4B Habitats

1 Describe a **tropical rainforest habitat**

2 Is a **consumer** **always a predator?**

PRODUCER

Science Chatterbox 3

5 Any **living thing**, whether a plant or animal is called?

lots of **light** and **water**, a **hot temperature** & **very rich, fertile soil**

an *organism*

NO **consumers** also include animals which **feed on plants**

a PREDATOR

6 An animal which **hunts** **other animals** is known as what?

8 **ALL** the **food chains** in a **habitat** are known as a ..?

food web

sometimes **no light** for **months**, **extremely cold**, **water** is ***usually frozen*** and any soil is usually covered by snow

prey

LOTS of LIGHT, a **hot temperature**, but very **little water** and very **poor soil**

7 What do you call an animal which is ***hunted* by another animal?**

PREY

4 Describe an **arctic habitat**

3 Describe a **desert habitat**

PREDATORS

Unit 4B

Habitats

Chatterbox 4 Level 4

POPULATION

Unit 4B Habitats

1 Where is the **wettest** place on earth?

2 Why is the term '**producer**' a **suitable name** for a green plant?

ECOSYSTEM

Chatterbox 4

Science

5 Where is the **driest** place on earth?

Cherrapunji in **India** - over **11 metres** of rain a year

the **Atacama Desert** - an average of **0.5mm** rain a **year**!

because plants are able to **produce their own food**, using the Sun's energy

an ECOSYSTEM

6 **ALL** the **living things**, the **soil** and the **weather** - found together in a **certain habitat** - are called?

8 Why can't ***banana trees*** **LIVE** in an ***arctic habitat?***

because they need a ***warm temperature*** lots of **water** lots of **light** and **rich soil**

scavengers, insects and **micro-organisms break it down** releasing **nutrients** back into the soil

the ***green plant***

if there are **too many predators**, the **prey will ALL be eaten**. CONSEQUENTLY, **all the predators** would then **starve** to death

7 In a food chain, the **arrows point away** from **what?**

ANIMALS

4 When a **predator** dies, **what happens?**

3 Why are there always **fewer** predators than **prey?**

PLANTS

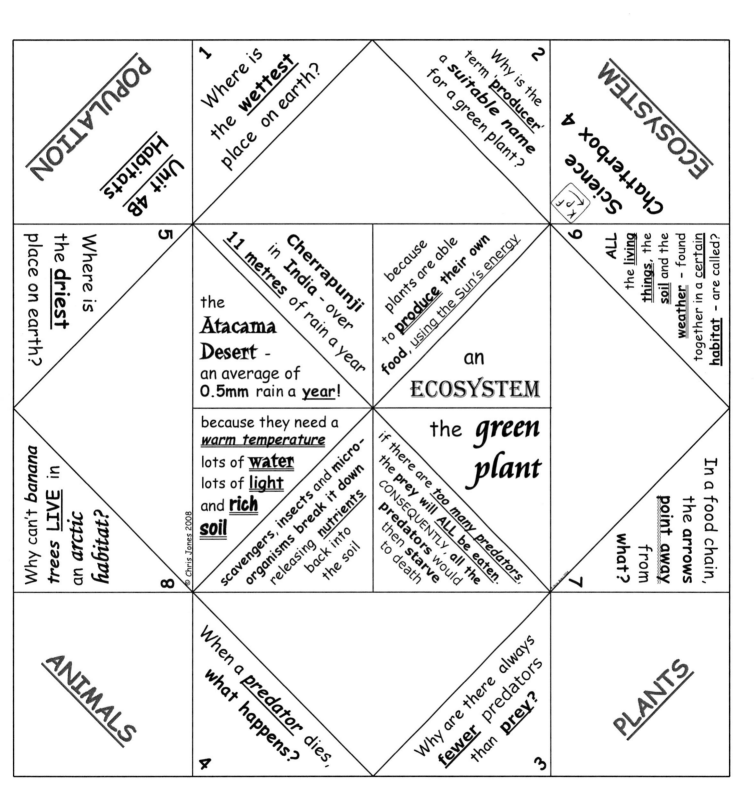

ESTUARY

Unit 4B Habitats

1 What is 'acid rain'?

2 How are coal burning power stations in Britain, able to **kill forest habitats** in parts of Sweden and Norway?

Science Chatterbox 5

HABITAT

5 In which **type of a habitat**, would you find a **cactus?**

when coal, petrol, oil, etc is burnt, a **gas** called **sulphur dioxide** is made. This joins to **water vapour** in the air to make weak **sulphuric acid**. This falls as rain

they produce a gas called **sulphur dioxide**, which becomes **acid rain**, which **poisons** the soil as it falls on those countries

6 The science name for butterflies and moths is **Lepidoptera.** How many different species are there?

a desert climate

there are more than **165,000** different species!!

© Chris Jones 2008

37 square miles
96 square km
24000 acres

ACID RAIN

lichen, woodlouse, nesting birds, flies, beetles, squirrels, moss, ants

fish, moss, toads, water spiders, reeds, snails, ducks, frogs, swans, kingfishers, dragonflies, algae

Trees provide a **habitat** for many living things. Can you name just eight of them?

8 How much of the Amazon Rainforest is cut down and burned, every **single day?**

MOUNTAIN

4 What is the **harmful rain** that dissolves limestone and marble and poisons lakes and rivers?

3 A pond provides a habitat for many living things. Name just twelve

7

MOORLAND

Unit 4C

Keeping Warm

Chatterbox 1   Level 3

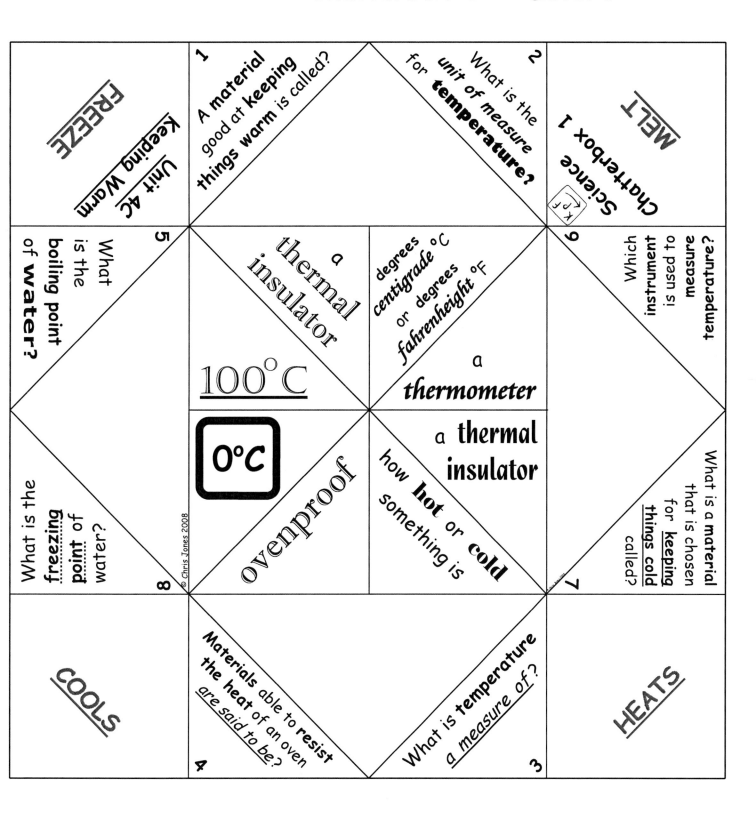

FREEZE

Keeping Warm Unit 4C

1 A material good at **keeping things warm** is called?

2 What is the unit of measure for **temperature?**

Science Chatterbox 1

MELT

a thermal insulator

degrees centigrade °C or degrees fahrenheight °F

Which instrument is used to measure **temperature?**

$100°C$

a thermometer

5 What is the boiling point of **water?**

a thermal insulator

© Chris Jones 2008

$0°C$

ovenproof

how **hot** or **cold** something is

What is a material that is chosen for **keeping things cold** called?

What is the **freezing point** of water?

8

7

COOLS

Materials able to **resist the heat** of an oven are said to be?

What is **temperature a measure of?**

HEATS

4

Unit 4C

Keeping Warm

Chatterbox 2 Level 3

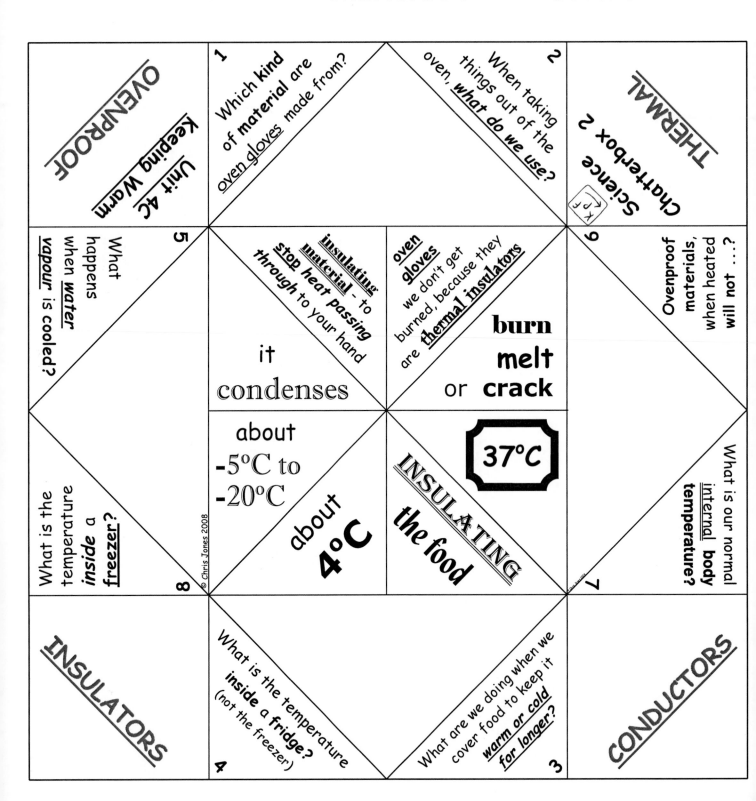

OVENPROOF

Unit 4C Keeping Warm

1 Which **kind** of **material** are oven gloves made from?

2 When taking things out of the oven, ***what do we use?***

THERMAL

Science Chatterbox 2

5 What happens when **water** **vapour** is cooled?

insulating material - to **stop heat passing through** to your hand

oven gloves we don't get burned, because they are **thermal insulators**

6 Ovenproof materials, when heated **will not . . .?**

it condenses

burn

melt

or **crack**

about

-5°C to

-20°C

about **4°C**

37°C

INSULATING the food

8 What is the temperature ***inside*** a **freezer?**

© Chris Jones 2008

7 What is our normal internal **body temperature?**

INSULATORS

4 What is the temperature **inside** a **fridge?** (not the freezer)

3 What are we doing when we cover food to keep it ***warm or cold for longer?***

CONDUCTORS

Unit 4C

Keeping Warm

Chatterbox 3 Level 4

THERMOS

Unit 4C Keeping Warm

INSULATION

Science Chatterbox 3

CARPET

POLYSTYRENE

1 If a cup of **hot** coffee is left standing, what **temperature** will it **eventually change to?**

2 A material that **allows heat** to easily **pass through** is called?

3 Why are hot drinks often contained in **polystyrene** cups?

4 Why are frying pans **made of metal?**

5 how warm is **room temperature?**

6 Why do some saucepans have **wooden** or **plastic handles?**

7 Why don't we wear a **suit of armour** to school?

8 Metal is a **thermal conductor**, what else does it **conduct?**

it will **lose heat** until it reaches **room temperature**

about **21°C**

a **thermal conductor**

because wood and plastic are **thermal insulators**

electricity

metal is a **thermal conductor** - so **heat passes quickly** from the cooker into the frying pan, which gets v. hot v. fast!

polystyrene is a **thermal insulator** - it keeps drinks hotter for longer (plus you don't burn your hand!)

because it's made from metal - a ***thermal conductor*** - which would ***take heat away from*** our body

Unit 4C

Keeping Warm

Chatterbox 4 Level 4

MEASURE

Unit 4C Keeping Warm

1 What makes **thermal insulators** **feel warm?**

2 Why are most windows **'double glazed'?**

CONDUCTORS

Science Chatterbox 4

5 How might you define, **'cold'?**

they are **full** of *air spaces*, and *air* is a **poor conductor of heat** - **therefore** **heat cannot pass through** easily

'cold' is the **'absence of heat'**

the **2** layers of glass **trap a layer of air**, which is a **poor** *conductor of heat* - so double glazing provides thermal insulation

to **insulate** us from the cold - **several layers** are an **excellent thermal insulator** from the cold

6 Why do we wear **several layers** of clothes on ***cold days?***

8 A **thermos flask** is used for keeping hot drinks hot! What else is it used for?

keeping cold drinks **cold!**

metal is a **thermal conductor** and *takes heat away* from your hand. So it **feels** cold

it's a ***thermal insulator*** - it ***prevents*** the **heat** in your hand from **escaping** - so it **feels warm**

a **thermal insulator** - because it **stops cold from getting** out - and **stops heat getting in!**

7 Why does carpet **feel warm** to the touch?

© Chris Jones 2008

METAL

4 In the classroom, why does a **metal** chair leg **feel** cold?

3 What would be a **good material** to *keep a cold drink cold?*

THERMOMETER

Unit 4C

Keeping Warm

Chatterbox 5 Level 4/5

CENTIGRADE

Keeping Warm

Unit 4C

DEGREES

Science Chatterbox 5

FAHRENHEIGHT

TEMPERATURE

1 What is cavity insulation?

2 What is a loft insulator?

3 Why does a woolly hat **feel warmer** than a cotton hat in winter?

4 What is the first response of the body, when it starts to get cold?

5 How could you **reduce** some of the noise coming from noisy neighbours?

6 Name **5 different** types of **thermal insulators** found in the home

7 Double glazing provides thermal insulation. **What other kind of insulation** does it provide?

8 What is the ***freezing point*** of **helium**? (almost the lowest temp. it's possible to reach!!)

a **foam** injected in the wall space between two houses. **It traps air as it hardens**. Therefore it's an excellent sound and heat insulator

fill the wall space with insulation foam. When the foam hardens, it acts as a **sound insulator**. Also, maybe lay thick carpets.

a material, which is used to line the floors of lofts and attics - to **prevent heat** from the rest of the house from **escaping**

carpet
curtains
double glazing
loft insulation
cavity insulation

-272°C

(**minus** 272 degrees!)

it shivers - the muscles rapidly contract and relax - a process that can generate lots of heat

sound insulation

the fibres that wool is made from, are able to trap **more air** than cotton fibres

© Chris Jones 2008

Unit 4D

Solids, Liquids and how they can be Separated

Chatterbox 1 Level 3

STATE

Unit 4D Solids, Liquids and Separating

1 Which **state of matter** is bicarbonate of soda?

2 What is a **filter?**

LIQUID

Science Chatterbox 1

5 A solid made of **very tiny pieces** is called a ...?

a solid

powder

a piece of scientific equipment used for **separating mixtures** containing undissolved solids

gas solid and liquid

6 What are the three states of matter?

8 Name the **process** where a **solid changes into a liquid**

melting

the solid breaks into pieces so small, they can't be seen with the naked eye

freezing

the temperature in the freezer is less than 0°C. It's about 4°C in the fridge so the ice has melted

7 Name the **process** where a **liquid changes into a solid**

© Chris Jones 2008

SOLID

4 When a **solid dissolves**, what happens?

3 Some ice cubes are taken out of a **freezer** and put into a **fridge**. **They melted. Why?**

GAS

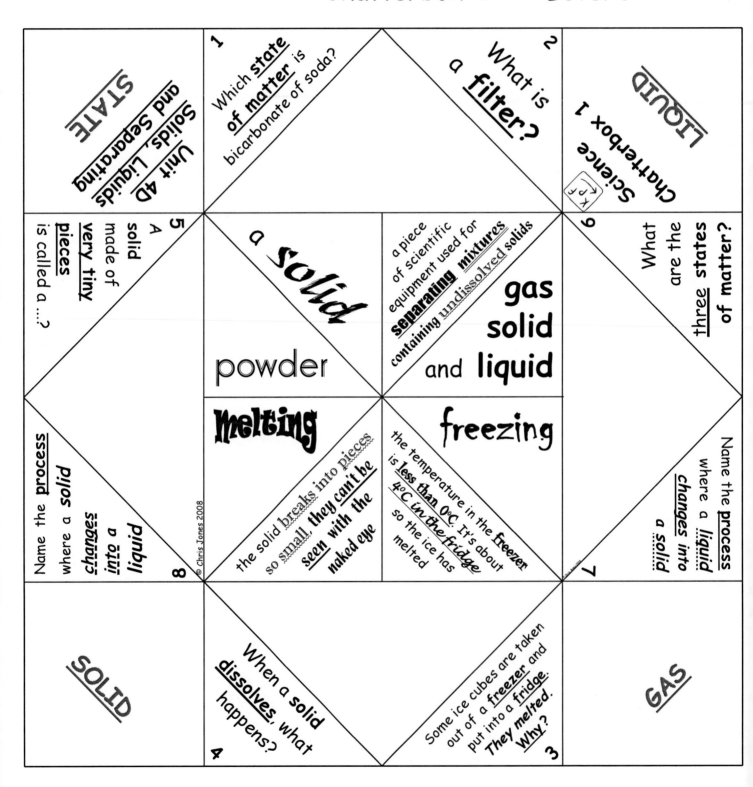

Unit 4D

Solids, Liquids and how they can be Separated

Chatterbox 2 Level 3

SIEVE

Unit 4D Solids, Liquids and Separating

1 What is **filter paper?**

2 What are the **properties** of a **liquid?**

FILTER

Science Chatterbox 2

5 What **happens** when a **material freezes?**

a special **sieve** - made with special paper, full of holes which are **microscopic in size**

it changes from the *liquid state* to the *solid state*

liquids have **no fixed shape**, have a **fixed volume**, can flow and take the shape of their container

nothing - sand can't **dissolve**

6 If sand is **mixed** with water, **what happens?**

What is a **sieve?** 8

a TYPE OF FILTER, with **large holes** to SEPARATE **different sized solids**

the water **tastes sweet** - **therefore**, the sugar must still be there

it changes from a solid state to a liquid state

solids have a **fixed volume**, are **not easily compressed** & retain their shape unless a force is applied

What **happens** when a **material melts?** 7

COLANDER

4 When sugar dissolves in water **you can't see it** - how do you know it is still there?

What are the **properties** of a **solid?** 3

NET

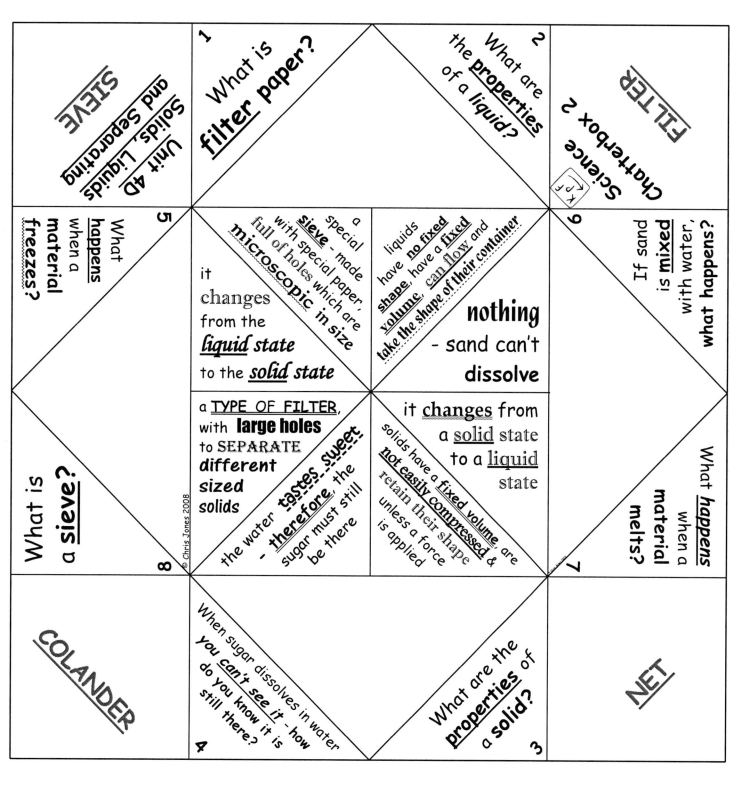

Unit 4D

Solids, Liquids and how they can be Separated

Chatterbox 3 Level 3

FREEZE

Unit 4D Solids, Liquids and Separating

1 Which is the odd one out: sugar, flour, salt, jelly?

2 What are the properties of a gas?

MELT

Science Chatterbox 3

5 Which is the odd one out: flour, sand, sugar or rice?

flour is the only solid which doesn't dissolve in water

sugar is the only solid that will dissolve in water

gases HAVE NO FIXED SHAPE can be compressed, and will fill the whole container they are in

a thermometer

6 Which instrument is temperature measured with?

8 At which temperature does water boil?

100°C

0°C

solidify

the volume remains the same, but its shape changes to the new container

7 What is another word for freeze?

EVAPORATE

4 At which temperature does water freeze?

3 What happens when a liquid is poured into a different container?

CONDENSATES

Unit 4D

Solids, Liquids and how they can be Separated

Chatterbox 4 Level 4

INSOLUBLE

Unit 4D Solids, Liquids and Separating

1 What is a **solution?**

2 If a solid has been **dissolved in water**, how is it able **to pass through** a filter?

DISSOLVES

Science Chatterbox 4

5 What does **'insoluble in water'** mean?

a liquid CONTAINING a **soluble solid which has completely dissolved**

the particles are **much smaller** than the MICROSCOPIC HOLES of the **filter paper** - and **easily pass through**

6 How might you **prevent** butter **melting on a hot day?**

a solid which **WILL NOT** DISSOLVE IN WATER (flour, chalk, sand, etc)

keep it in the fridge - the temperature is about 4°C (less than butter's melting point)

8 What is a **solute?**

a material which **can be dissolved** (eg, salt, sugar)

NO, it is still there, but the particles are **too small to be seen with the naked eye**

a **liquid** which is **able to dissolve** a **soluble solid**

solids - they all have **fixed volumes and shapes** - **unless a force is applied**

7 What is a **solvent?**

© Chris Jones 2008

REVERSIBLE

4 When a solid **dissolves**, has it disappeared?

3 What are **sponges, metal, ice, rock, paper** and **chewing gum** all examples of?

IRREVERSIBLE

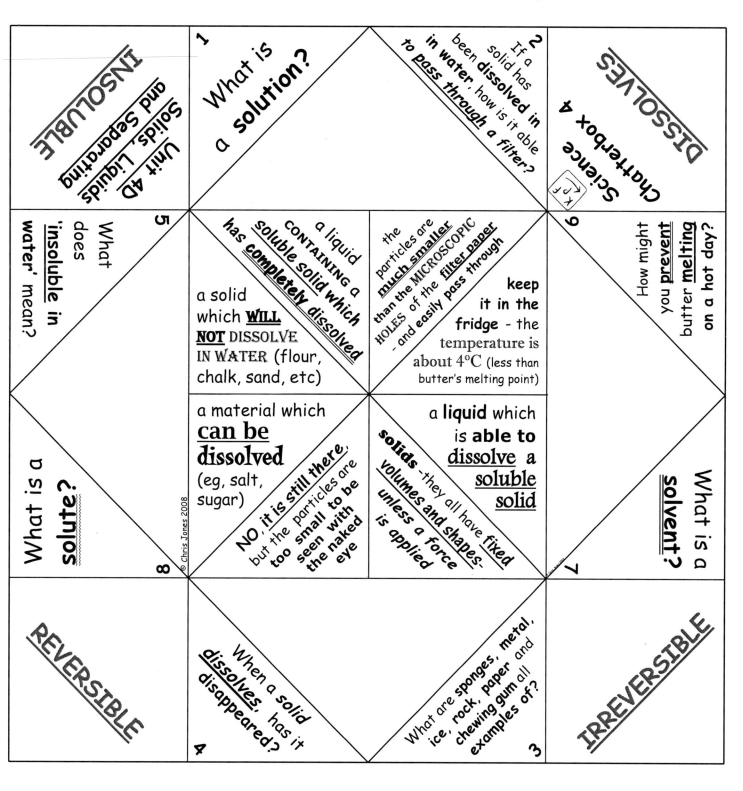

Unit 4D

Solids, Liquids and how they can be Separated

Chatterbox 5 Level 4

HOLES

Unit 4D Solids, Liquids and Separating

FILTER

Science Chatterbox 5

MICROSCOPIC

SEPARATION

1 What is used to **prevent** your cup filling with **tea leaves?**

the tea is in a **tea bag** - it **acts as a filter**, allowing the flavour **through**, but **not the** leaves

2 What are **petrol, treacle, ink and syrup examples** of?

LIQUIDS -they can all flow, have a **fixed volume, but no fixed shape.** They cannot be compressed.

3 **Powders can be poured. Are they liquids?**

NO! - powders are **tiny solid pieces**, each piece **keeps its shape** UNLESS a force is applied

4 **Which equipment could be used to separate sand from water?**

a **funnel with filter paper** pour the mixture in **-the sand remains in the filter paper**

5 Which is the **odd one out**; **butter, a plate, treacle or sugar?**

treacle is a liquid- the others are **solids**

6 What is an **insoluble substance?**

a **solid** which **does not dissolve** in water

7 How can you **separate** a goldfish from its pond?

use a net! it's a **sieve**

8 How do you **drain water from pasta?**

use a **colander** it's a **sieve**

© Chris Jones 2008

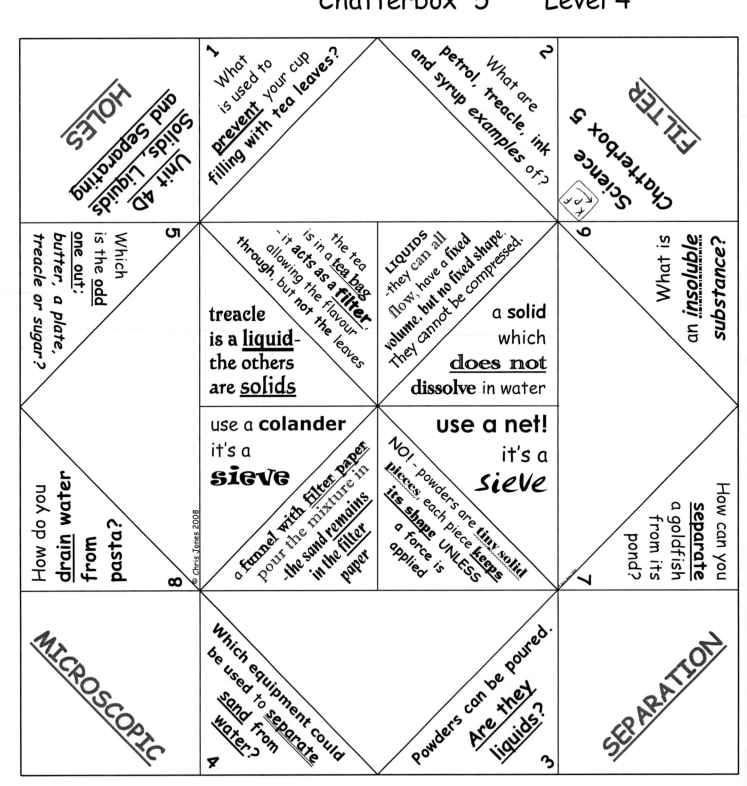

Unit 4D

Solids, Liquids and how they can be Separated

Chatterbox 6 Level 4

Unit 4D Solids, Liquids and Separating

REVERSIBLE

1 Which **piece** of **equipment** could be used to **separate** a **mixture** of sugar and rice?

2 **Tungsten** is a **metal used in light bulbs** - what is its **melting point?**

Science Chatterbox 6

CHANGES

5 At which **temperature** does **iron melt?**

a **sieve** could be used - the **sugar passes through** the **small holes** leaving the rice in the sieve

1300°C

about 3500°C

honey, washing up liquid, orange squash, (can you think of more?)

6 Give **three examples** of **liquids** that **dissolve** in water

Tungsten is a **metal**, at which **temperature** does it **boil** and **change** to a **gas?** 8

about 5500°C

a **reversible change**

-64°C (minus 64) it is the **only metal** which is a **liquid** at room temp!

lava

7 **Mercury is a metal - which temperature** does it **melt at?**

CONDENSATION

4 What **kind of a change** is water **freezing into ice - THEN - melting back into water?**

Rock is **usually a solid**, what **name** do we give it when it is **liquid** and **runny?** 3

EVAPORATION

Unit 4D

Solids, Liquids and how they can be Separated
Chatterbox 7   Level 4

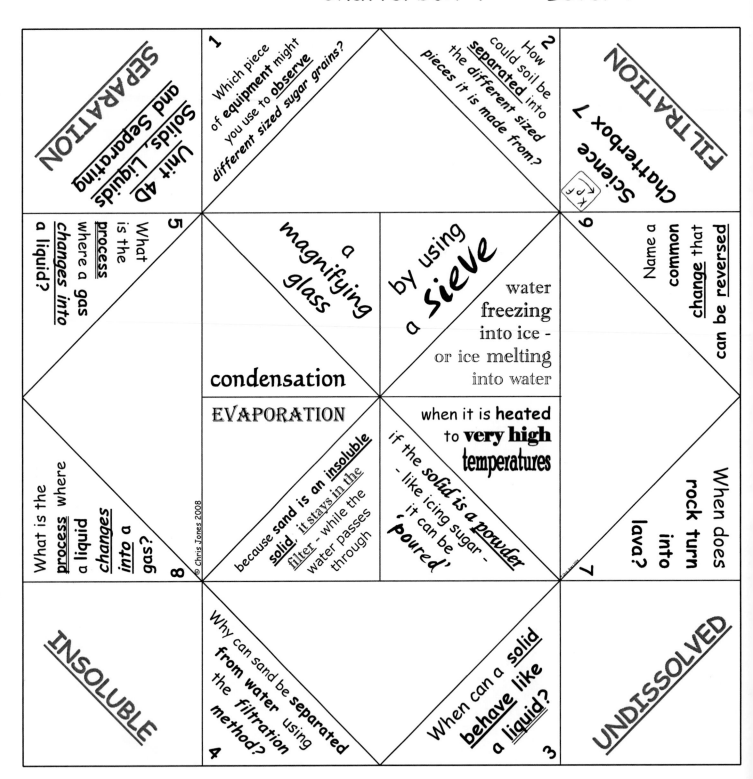

SEPARATION

Unit 4D
Solids, Liquids and Separating

1 Which piece of **equipment** might you use to <u>observe</u> different sized *sugar grains*?

2 How could soil be **separated** into the different sized pieces it is made from?

FILTRATION

Science Chatterbox 7

5 What is the <u>process</u> where a **gas** <u>changes into</u> a liquid?

a magnifying glass

by using a *sieve*

water freezing into ice - or ice melting into water

6 Name a **common** <u>change</u> that <u>can be reversed</u>

condensation

EVAPORATION

when it is **heated** to **very high temperatures**

if the <u>solid is a powder</u> - like icing sugar - it can be '**poured**'

© Chris Jones 2008

8 What is the <u>process</u> where a liquid **changes** <u>into a</u> **gas**?

because **sand is an insoluble** <u>solid</u>, <u>it stays in the</u> <u>filter</u> - while the water passes through

When does **rock** turn into **lava**?

7

INSOLUBLE

4 Why can sand be **separated** **from water** using the *filtration* **method**?

When can a **solid** behave like a **liquid**?

3

UNDISSOLVED

Unit 4D

Solids, Liquids and how they can be Separated

Chatterbox 8 Level 5

SOLUBLE

Unit 4D Solids, Liquids and Separating

1 Explain what happens ***inside*** a ***material*** when it **melts**

2 How could a ***mixture*** of **pebbles, sand and salt** be **separated?**

DISSOLVES

Science Chatterbox 8

5 How do the particles (atoms) ***in a solid*** **behave?**

as a solid the **particles are joined with bonds**. As it heats, the particles begin **vibrating violently**, break the bonds and **start moving freely**. IT'S MELTED

they're tightly packed - **strong bonds between them hold them together** - they can only vibrate

1. a sieve will separate the pebbles 2. mix with water - the salt dissolves 3. separate sand using filter 4. evaporate water to leave the salt

you could use a MAGNET to ***attract the steel nails***, (*aluminium does not attract to magnets*)

6 How could you **separate** a mixture of ***steel nails and aluminium screws?***

8 How do the **particles** in ***a liquid*** **behave?**

the particles are **less tightly packed** & **slide between each other** - like sand in an egg timer

particles are **widely spread out, moving around in all directions** - like sand in a sand-storm

© Chris Jones 2008

OIL is **lighter than water** so it **floats on the surface** - *carefully pour the oil layer away*

water particles **crash into the solid, breaking off pieces until they're too small to be seen with the naked eye**

7 How could you **separate** a ***mixture of*** **water and cooking oil?**

SOLUTE

4 How do the **particles** ***in a gas*** **behave?**

3 **What actually happens** when a ***soluble solid*** such as sugar, **dissolves in water?**

SOLUTION

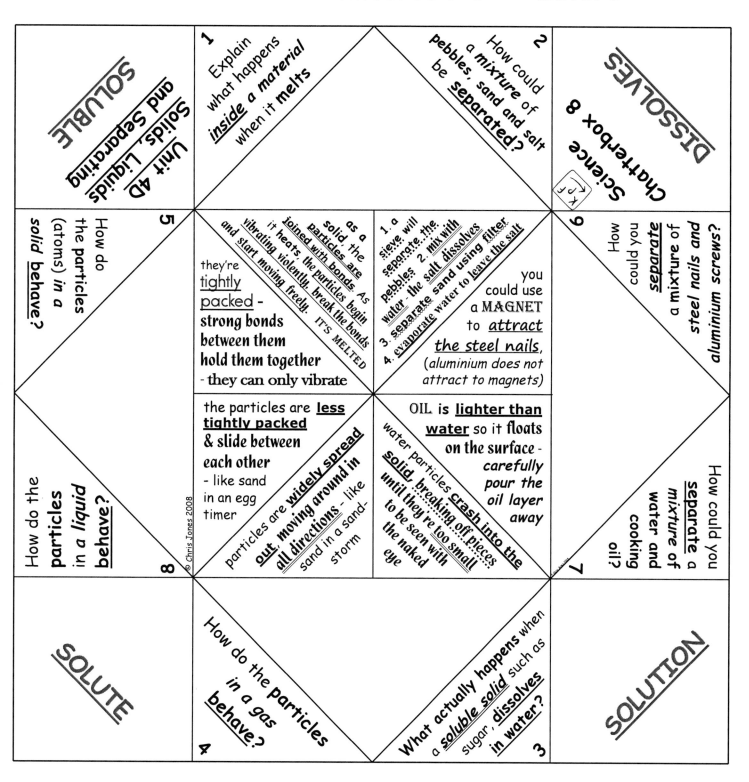

Unit 4E

Friction

Chatterbox 1 Level 3

FORCE

Unit 4E Friction

1 Which **instrument** is **used to measure forces?**

2 When you quickly **rub your hands together,** what happens?

FRICTION

Science Chatterbox 1

5 What do we call **friction in air?**

a **forcemeter** (or **Newton meter**)

they heat up

6 Name a force **beginning with 'F'.**

air resistance

friction

Newtons

friction

8 Which **unit of measure** is used for forces?

a **force** which **slows moving objects** (it also **produces heat**)

WATER RESISTANCE

7 Name the **FORCE** which **slows a moving object**

© Chris Jones 2008

CONTACT

4 What is **friction?**

3 What do we call **friction in water?**

SURFACE

Friction

Chatterbox 2   Level 3

BALANCE

Unit 4E Friction

1 What is another name for a **forcemeter**?

2 What is **water resistance**?

Science Chatterbox 2

WEIGHT

What is the 'important' **moving part** in a **forcemeter**?

When you **rub your hands together**, why do they **heat up**? 5

a Newton meter

friction caused by water - a speedboat will slow down then stop - unless, its engine is running

6

because of friction

the **spring**

high friction

LOW FRICTION

Rough surfaces produce..?

when **two surfaces** **come into contact** with each other

friction caused by air - that's why aircraft are pointed - to **reduce** **resistance**

Smooth surfaces produce? 7

8

© Chris Jones 2008

SPRING

When does **friction** occur? 4

What is **air resistance?** 3

NEWTONMETER

Unit 4E

Friction

Chatterbox 3 Level 3

NEWTONS

Unit 4E Friction

1 When does **water resistance** occur?

2 When does **air resistance** occur?

MEASURE

Science Chatterbox 3

5 Why are planes and rockets **pointed in shape?**

when the SURFACE of a MOVING OBJECT comes into contact with water

when the surface of a moving object is in contact with air

6 Why are fish usually **pointed** and **streamlined?**

to reduce air resistance they're streamlined to cut through the air & need less energy to move

to **reduce water resistance** whilst they are swimming

100g

Sir Isaac Newton

8 How many grams **equals** a force of 1 Newton 1N=□g?

their shape is 'pointed' and streamlined

when a **force pulls on it**, the spring inside **stretches** and the **amount** of **force is shown on the scale**

7 Which *scientist* is the **unit of measure** for **force** named after?

SCALES

4 How are fish **adapted** to **reduce water resistance** in the sea?

3 How does a **force meter work?**

FORCEMETER

Unit 4E

Friction

Chatterbox 4   Level 4

ARROWS

Unit 4E Friction

1 What is meant by 'good grip'?

2 Which falls faster, a **small** or a **large** parachute?

Science Chatterbox 4

DIRECTION

5 What can be used to **reduce** the **friction** between two surfaces?

there is enough **friction** between two surfaces, to **prevent them sliding** over each other

a **lubricant** such as oil

a small parachute - there's **less surface** for the air to resist - so **LESS FRICTION** - it falls faster

to REDUCE FRICTION - so they are **easier** to pull out

6 The surfaces of classroom trays and their storage space are usually smooth. Why?

Which **symbols** are used to show the **direction** forces are **acting**?

arrows

because there is more **air resistance**, which *slows* you down

8

© Chris Jones 2008

because water resistance **slows you down**

shoe B, because it's a sports shoe - its sole has the **best grip**

Why is it **hard** to **walk fast** in a swimming pool?

7

GRIP

4 Why does **walking into the wind on a windy day** need more energy?

3 Shoe A is a sandal, Shoe B is a trainer. Which will need **most force** to pull?

GRAVITY

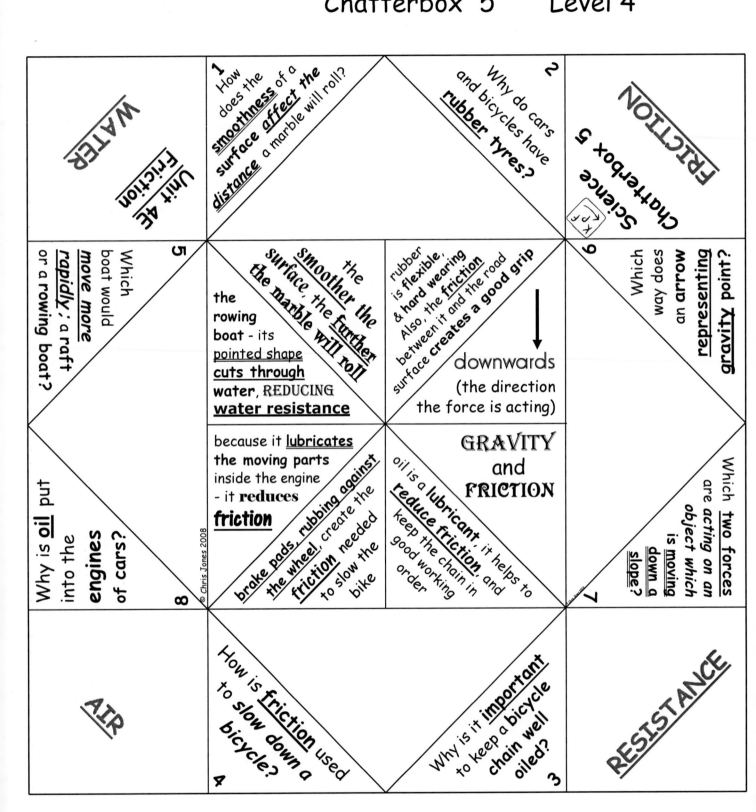

WATER

Unit 4E
Friction

1 How does the *smoothness* of a *surface affect the distance* a marble will roll?

2 Why do cars and bicycles have **rubber tyres?**

FRICTION

Science
Chatterbox 5

5 Which boat would *move more rapidly*; a raft or a rowing boat?

the smoother the surface, the *further* the marble will roll

the rowing boat - its *pointed shape* **cuts through** water, REDUCING **water resistance**

rubber is flexible, & hard wearing Also, the **friction** between it and the road surface **creates a good grip**

↓

downwards (the direction the force is acting)

6 Which way does an arrow *representing gravity point?*

because it **lubricates** the moving parts inside the engine - it **reduces friction**

brake pads, rubbing against the wheel, create the **friction** needed to slow the bike

oil is a **lubricant**, it helps to **reduce friction**, and keep the chain in good working order

GRAVITY and FRICTION

Which **two forces** are acting on an *object which* is **moving down a slope?**

Why is **oil** put into the *engines of cars?*

© Chris Jones 2008

8

7

AIR

How is **friction** used to **slow down a bicycle?**

Why is it **important** to keep a bicycle *chain well oiled?*

RESISTANCE

4

Unit 4E

Friction

Chatterbox 6 Level 4

EQUAL

Unit 4E Friction

1 Will a toy car **travel further** on a **smooth** or **rough** surface? Explain why

2 Is it easier to pull an object **along a school desk** or **along sandpaper?**

BALANCED

Science Chatterbox 6

5 What happens to a bicycle if **oil is spilt on a road?**

it **travels further** on a **smooth surface** - there is **LESS FRICTION** between the wheels and surface

oil is a **lubricant**, which **reduces friction** between the tyre and road - the bike probably **skids!**

the school desk, because the smooth surface **creates less friction**

the **faster the speed** of a bicycle the **longer the time** it takes to stop

6 How does the **speed** of a bicycle, **affect** the **time** it takes to stop?

8 What **effect** does **increasing the mass, have** on the **force needed** to **move** an **object?**

© Chris Jones 2008

greater the mass the **greater the force** needed to move it

the **steeper the slope**, the **greater the force needed** to pull an object up it

the children **wear trainers**, with a **good grip** - so they don't slip over!

a squeak is caused by two surfaces rubbing, so you need **to reduce friction by lubricating it** (use grease or oil)

7 How is **friction useful** for children in outdoor PE lessons?

SURFACE AREA

4 How does the **steepness** of a slope, **affect** the **force needed** to pull an object up it?

3 What **must be done** to **stop a door squeaking?**

UNBALANCED

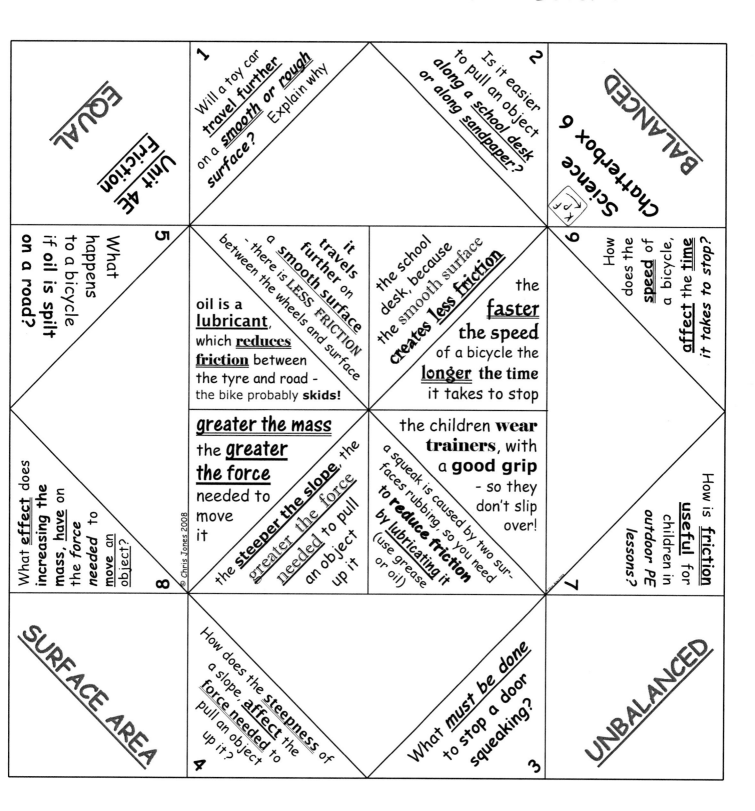

Unit 4E

Friction

Chatterbox 7 Level 5

SMOOTH

Unit 4E Friction

1 Which forces **need to be balanced** for a boat to float?

2 Which **variable affects the time taken** for **different** parachutes to fall to earth?

REDUCED

Science Chatterbox 7

5 Which **two forces** are **acting** on **a boat floating on a lake?**

1. gravity **pulling down**
2. upthrust **pushing up**

both need to be balanced

gravity, **which pulls it down** ↓ and upthrust, which **pushes it up** ↑

the **size** of the parachute

more surface area → MORE AIR RESISTANCE → the **slower** they fall

with skates, -they have blades with **less surface area** **- so less friction**

6 Would you **slide further on ice;** wearing **skates** or wearing **Wellington boots?**

8 Which **variable affects** the time it takes for **different spinners to fall?**

*the **size** of the **wings***

the larger the wings, → more air resistance → slower they fall

a force could; **speed it up**, **slow it down**, make it change direction or **stop it**

they are **BALANCED**

the **laces!** -when you tie them together, **friction** stops them loosening and coming undone!

7 When an object is **not moving**, what can you **state** about the **forces?**

STREAMLINED

4 **A force acting** on a **moving object** can have **4 effects**. *What are they?*

3 The **sole** of a **shoe** has **grip** - where else is **friction working?**

LUBRICATED

Unit 4F

Circuits and Conductors

Chatterbox 1 Level 3

MOTOR

Unit 4F Circuits and Conductors

1 What does an **electrical** appliance **need** to work?

2 Name **three** electrical appliances that **change** electricity into **light**

BULB

Science Chatterbox 1

5 Name **3 electrical appliances** that **use mains power**

it must be **connected** to a complete circuit with electricity flowing through

vacuum cleaner, fridge-freezer, electric cooker

torches light bulbs computer monitors

TV, radio, vacuum cleaner

6 Name three **electrical appliances** that **change** *electricity to sound*

8 Which 5 other **forms of energy** can *electricity* be *changed* into?

© Chris Jones 2008

heat, movement magnetism, sound, light

radio controlled car, washing machine, electric drill

TORCH, I-POD, MOBILE PHONE

ELECTRIC COOKER, MICROWAVE, TOASTER

7 Name **3 electrical appliances** that **use battery power**

APPLIANCE

4 Name **three electrical devices** that **change** *electricity into movement*

3 Name **three electrical devices** that **change** *electricity into* **heat**

BUZZER

Unit 4F

Circuits and Conductors

Chatterbox 2 Level 3

Unit 4F Circuits and Conductors

COPPER

1 What is used to **control the flow** of **electricity in a circuit?**

2 Which is the **odd one out**; - plastic ruler, cork, aluminium foil, a rubber?

METAL

Science Chatterbox 2

5 Which material is the **best** **electrical conductor ?**

a switch

metal

the foil it is the **only** **electrical conductor**

because **metal** is an **electrical conductor**

6 Explain why wires are **made from metal**

8 What **travels** **around** a **complete circuit?**

electricity

light and **sound** energy plus a small amount of **heat** energy as well

ELECTRICAL APPLIANCES

metal wires

7 A toaster, kettle and bulb are **examples** of **what?**

WIRE

4 A television **changes** **electricity** into **which** **other forms of energy?**

3 What does electricity **flow through** as it **travels around** a **circuit?**

CONDUCTOR

Unit 4F

Circuits and Conductors

Chatterbox 3 Level 3

CONTROL

Unit 4F Circuits and Conductors

1 What is the **purpose** of a **switch**?

2 If there is a **break in a circuit** then the electricity **will not** ....?

SWITCH

Science Chatterbox 3

5 A **flow of electricity** is called a ...?

to **control** the **flow of electricity** *around a circuit*

current

flow

a PLUS and a MINUS SIGN (+ and -)

6 Which **symbols** are found on **all batteries?**

8 Wires are usually made of this **metal**, because it is a **good conductor**

© Chris Jones 2008

copper

it needs electricity to be **flowing through it**

CELLS

because it's safer - an AA **battery** is 1.5 volts the **mains** is 240 volts

7 A battery is made of **two or more what?**

OPEN

4 What does an **electrical appliance need** to work?

3 In school, **why do we investigate using batteries?**

CLOSED

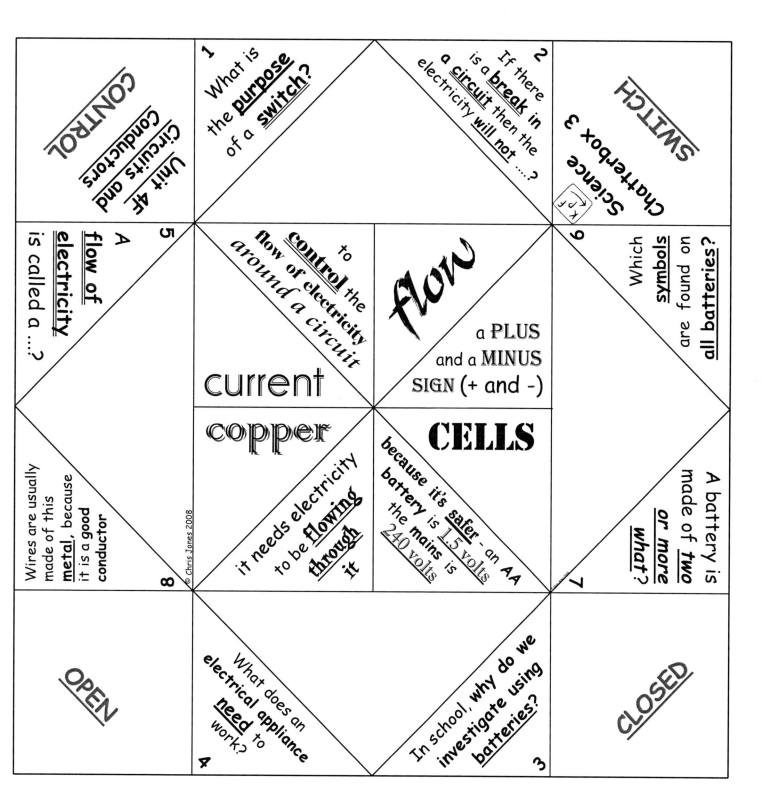

Unit 4F

Circuits and Conductors

Chatterbox 4 Level 3

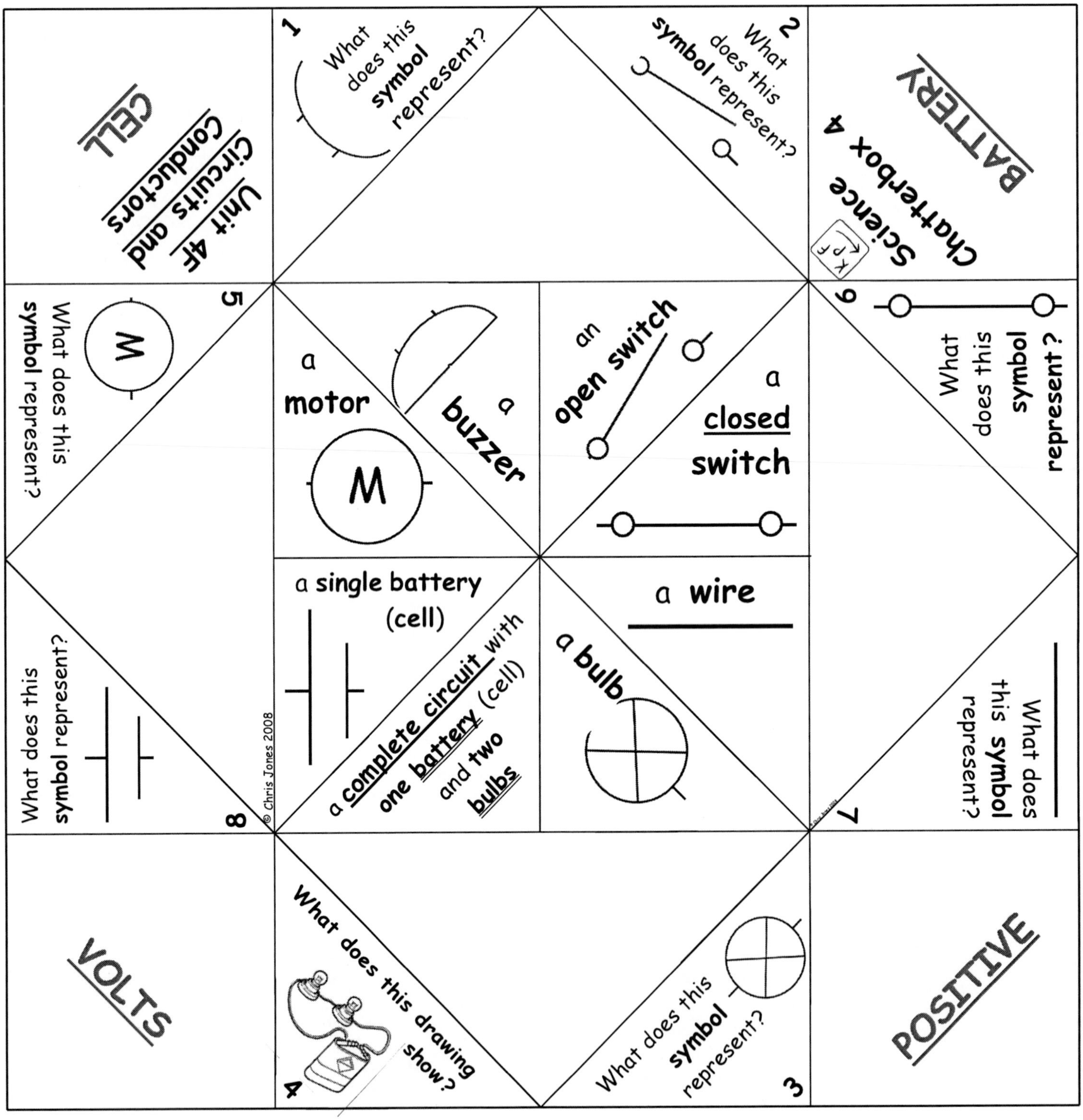

Unit 4F

Circuits and Conductors

Chatterbox 5 Level 4

COMPLETE

Unit 4F Circuits and Conductors

1 How could you **change** the **number of batteries** to make a **bulb brighter?**

2 How could you **change** the **number of batteries** to make a **bulb dimmer?**

CIRCUIT

Science Chatterbox 5

5 Explain why we use **symbols** to draw **circuit diagrams**

add MORE batteries

using **symbols** makes them **quick** to draw and very **easy to understand**

take away batteries

use **thicker** wire or use **shorter** wire

6 How could you **change** the **wires** in a **circuit** to make a **bulb brighter?**

8 How could you **change a wire** to make a bulb **dimmer?**

use **thinner** wire or use **longer** wire

a material which **DOESN'T ALLOW** electricity **to flow through**

YES, because the **switch** is **'ON'** so electricity can **flow** around the **circuit**

a material which **allows** electricity to **flow through**

7 In a circuit, **will a** bulb light, if a **switch** is **closed?**

© Chris Jones 2008

ELECTRICITY

4 What is an **electrical insulator?**

3 What is an **electrical conductor?**

FLOW

Unit 4F

Circuits and Conductors

Chatterbox 6 Level 4

SYMBOLS

Unit 4F Circuits and Conductors

1 What does the **dimmer switch** in a radio **control?**

2 Explain why wires are usually **covered** in **plastic** or **rubber**

DIAGRAM

Science Chatterbox 6

5 How does a **dimmer switch** work?

the **volume** of the sound

it REDUCES **the flow** of electricity - it is a '***resistor***'

for safety - these materials are good **electrical insulators** - so electricity cannot flow through them

a circuit diagram

6 What is a drawing using **symbols** to **represent** a circuit called?

The **end of the battery** with the **plus (+) sign** is called the? 8

© Chris Jones 2008

POSITIVE POLE

material that **allows some** electricity through, **but not all**

4.5V

copper, because it is an **excellent conductor** and is **very flexible**

How is a battery containing **three 1.5V cells labelled?** 7

SERIES

4 What is an **electrical resistor?**

Which **metal** are ***most wires made from and why?*** 3

PARALLEL

Unit 4F

Circuits and Conductors

Chatterbox 7 Level 4

BRIGHTER

Unit 4F Circuits and Conductors

BULB

Science Chatterbox 7

1 How do the **number** of **batteries** AFFECT the **brightness** of a **bulb?**

2 Give **4 ways** to **reduce** the **brightness** of a bulb

5 Name some **appliances** which use **dimmer** switches

6 Name **two** ***types*** of circuit

the **more batteries**, the BRIGHTER THE BULB (but too many and it will blow!)

lights, televisions, radios, drills, electric cookers, toasters, etc

lengthen the wire, use **thinner** wire, add more bulbs, **take away a battery**

parallel and **series**

add a battery - or ***use shorter wire*** - or use **thicker** wire

the THICKER the wire the BRIGHTER the bulb

the *longer* the wire, the *dimmer* the bulb

the **higher** the number of **bulbs**, the **dimmer** they will be

8 Give **3 ways** to **increase** the **brightness** of a bulb

7 How does the **length** of a **wire** ***affect*** how **bright** a bulb is?

© Chris Jones 2008

SHORTER

4 How does the **thickness** of a **wire** ***affect*** the **brightness** of a bulb?

3 How do the **number of bulbs** in a circuit, **affect** their **brightness?**

THICKER

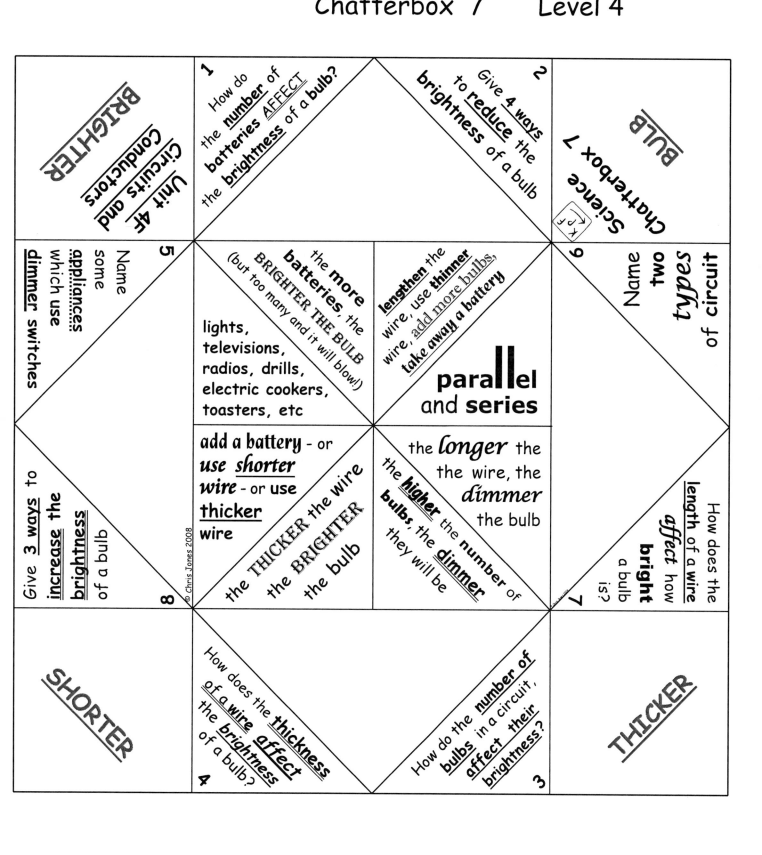

Unit 4F

Circuits and Conductors

Chatterbox 8 Level 5

TUNGSTEN

Unit 4F Circuits and Conductors

1 In a **series** circuit, what happens when a **bulb** is **removed**?

2 **How** does a bulb **actually** light?

FILAMENT

Science Chatterbox 8

5 What is the name given to the **thin metal part of the bulb**, that actually lights?

there is **just one circuit**, so if a **bulb** is REMOVED, the **circuit** is **broken** - and they all go off

the filament

billions of **electrons** squeeze through the **thin filament**, and cause **friction**, making it **heat up so much that it gives out light**

about **3500°C**

6 What is the **melting point** of **tungsten**?

8 Which **metal** is the **filament** of a bulb **made from?**

tungsten

a **SERIES circuit**

a **parallel circuit** because the lights come on at **different times**

the rest of the bulbs **remain lit**, because there is **more than one circuit**

7 Do traffic lights have a **series** or **parallel** circuit?

ELECTRONS

4 **Which circuit** do you have, if components are **joined one after another** like a daisy chain?

3 If a bulb is **removed** from a **parallel circuit**, what will **happen**?

FLOWING

Blank Chatterbox

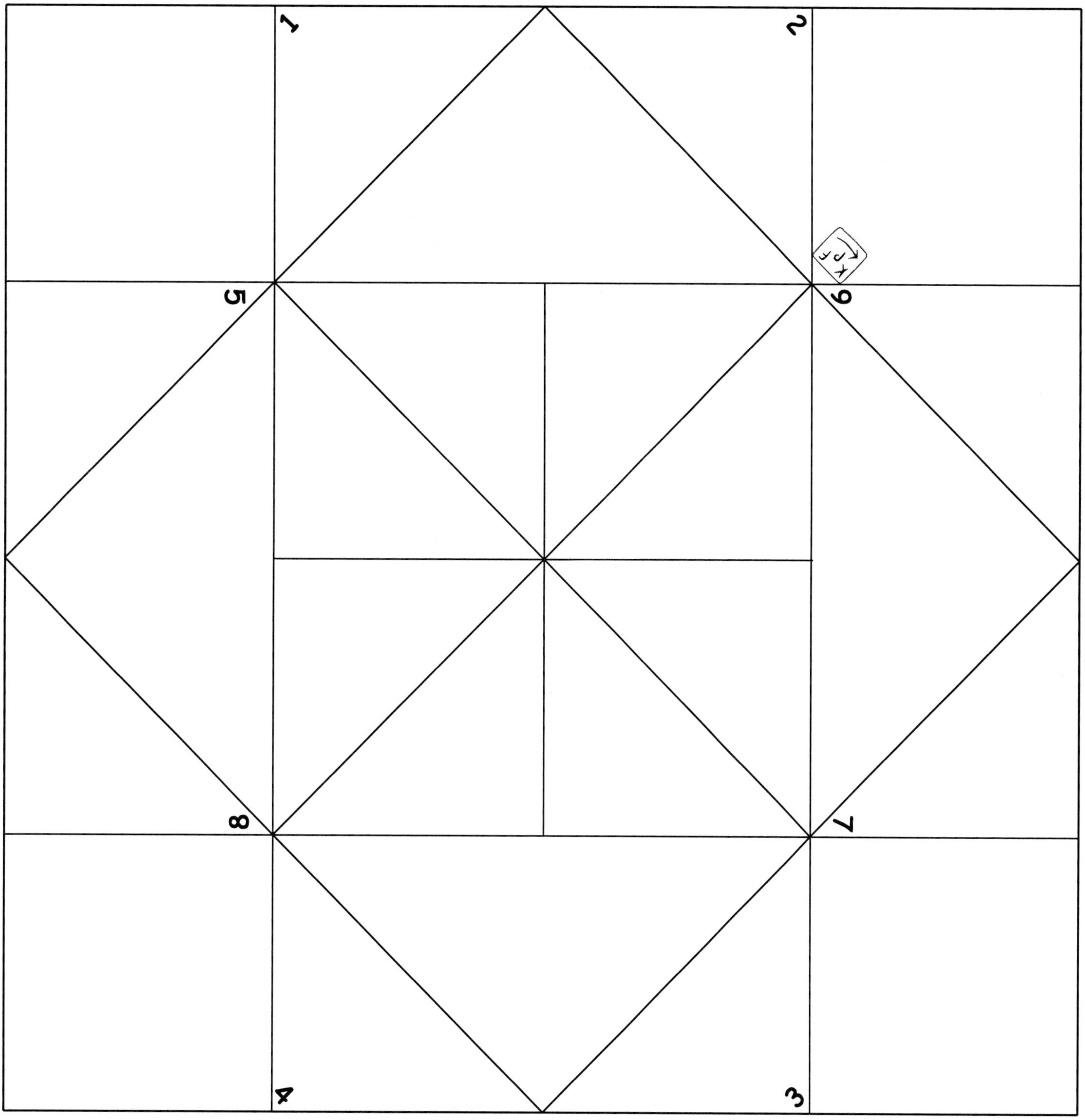

Key Facts
Publications